17.

to Paul,

Here in the Cull Valley

+ Up the Mariners! (p 129)

John

John Wheatcroft

Stairwell Books

Published by Stairwell Books
70 Barbara Drive
Norwalk
CT 06851 USA

161 Lowther Street
York, YO31 7LZ

ISBN: 978-1-939269-40-9

Cover design: Richard McDougall of Creative Squeeze
Layout design: Alan Gillott

To Kay

And in memory of my mum Ada (1925-2015)
and dad Derek (1924-2016)

Here in the Cull Valley, principal characters

Teddy Beresford, a journalist
Dr Valerie Beresford, Teddy's mother
Dr Philip Beresford, Teddy's father
Julia Yates
Anthony Yates

Friends of Teddy Beresford:

Henry 'Hank' Hawley (d 1998)
Paul 'Paolo' Hopkinson
Ruth Nolan (née Fitzpatrick)
Rory Nolan
Rachel Waterfall
Tom Waterfall (né Hogg)

Journalists on the Cull Valley Evening Gazette, a newspaper in West Yorkshire:

Stan Cartwright, former news editor
Hazel Moses, women's page editor
Gavin Layton, news reporter
Jeannie Derby, news reporter
Frances 'Doc' Jekyll, chief sub-editor
Kenneth 'Chuck' Thrower, deputy editor
Mark McClair, editor
Jim Stafford, former sports editor

Writers for the National Diary, a newspaper that exists only in the head of Teddy Beresford:

Teddy/ Henry Hawley/ Jenny Dudley/ Jon Stretford/ Anthony Yates/ Freddie Tilson/ Park Ranger/ Tom Waterfall/ Heather Margolis

Charity shop workers:

Cath Wilson, Ray Hutton, Barbara Machin, Andy Dougan, Julia Yates

Also:

Sally Merrens, midwife and sister of Hazel Moses
Melanie Gold, cognitive behavioural therapist
Gill Swallow, journalist in terrorist incident
Boris Becker, a West German tennis player
Jeffrey Woodworth, a musician and entrepreneur

PROLOGUE

Monday August 31 2009

The A8814, West Yorkshire, 11-27AM

I'm about to die, a fate that I don't deserve for all my faults. You might even begin to feel some sympathy for me as this tale unfolds. I'd advise, mind you, against getting too emotionally involved; flipping to the last few pages in the hope that some unlikely providential intervention is going to save me will only lead to disappointment.

However, the last thing I want to do is put you off. Stay with me and, in six months' time, your patience should be rewarded with a comforting postscript to my story. I just wish I could be there to see it. But, as an atheist, I'm pretty damned sure that these next few seconds are the last I will know of this or any other life.

You will be reading about my death in tomorrow's *Cull Valley Evening Gazette*. Some who know me will reflect that this is a strange end for a young man who's had a smooth passage through life as the decent-looking, artistically-inclined and sporty son of two local doctors.

Only the other night I was saying to an acquaintance in the pub: "I've been stabbed in the back and lost my job. This is the worst thing that's happened to me for years."

He said: "Lucky you. If that's as bad as it's got, you must have had an easy ride, Matey."

He'd change his tune if he could see me now.

I am in an old Ford Anglia, being driven by my ex-girlfriend, Julia. 'I have been driven by' would be nearer the mark, because her car has tipped over the barrier, and seems to be hanging in mid-air.

3

God knows why I wasn't more careful, I should never have let the baby business slip out.

"Oh Jesus," says Julia's husband, Anthony, from the front passenger seat. Two bananas and a foil package are also airborne. We were going – or so I thought – on a picnic.

As the bright-red Anglia, Julia's pride and joy, begins its nosedive to the embankment, Anthony's newspaper hits the windscreen.

How bloody appropriate, I spent most of my life in newspapers. Well, two newspapers; the real one in Yorkshire, where I earned my living, and the *National Diary*, the fantasy paper where I played out the story of my life. That's the one that allowed me to analyse everything that happened to me; the one that let me speculate on everybody else's life; the one I started writing when I was a kid.

1986 it would have been…Boris Becker (title holder) versus Me....

The National Diary

A new paper starts with great news for all patriotic Britons!

Number 1, July 1986

Teddy follows in Fred's footsteps

Perry sees Yorkshire teenager triumph in 'greatest final'
By Our Sporting Correspondent, aged 11

At long last! Britain has its first male Wimbledon tennis champion for precisely half a century!

In beating defending champion Boris Becker after five of the most exciting sets the famous arena in SW19 has ever seen, unseeded Teddy Beresford achieved a feat last seen in 1936.

The final score 5-7, 6-3, 6-2, 5-7, 8-6 tells its own story about what a close encounter this turned out to be. The deafening crowd, keen to roar the 17-year-old Yorkshire man to success, must have thought it was not going to be Beresford's day on the evidence of the early exchanges.

In fact, when Becker stormed into a 3-0 first-set lead, Beresford seemed to be the calmest Briton in the stadium, almost as if he knew his game plan would pay dividends in the end. Although he narrowly lost the first set, Beresford took the next two so decisively that Becker occasionally found his opponent almost unplayable!

However, the West German – ironically also unseeded when he won last year – was not the defending Wimbledon champion for nothing. Finding his feet again in the fourth set he then threatened to overwhelm the tiring Beresford. The fifth set ebbed and flowed with a game break apiece and there was really nothing to choose at the end between these two fine players. A revitalised Beresford went on the offensive again and finally won the match with a fantastically daring backhand volley. Then both men rushed to the net to embrace one another!

In the crowd, there were tears of joy from Beresford's mother, Valerie, a General Practitioner and former Yorkshire county player, who first encouraged her son to pick up a tiny racket when he was just a little three-year-old.

Becker, who had never under-estimated his opponent, said later: "I knew it would be close. I don't like losing, but it's a privilege to have been part of such a magnificent match. I'm sure that Teddy will be a great opponent on court and friend off it for many years to come. The great sport of tennis was a winner today!"

One of the first to congratulate Beresford afterwards was Fred Perry himself. The Stockport-born former champion said: "I never thought I would live to see this day. Teddy's triumph, in perhaps the greatest final of the modern era, will encourage a new generation of British tennis players. He will be a wonderful role model, and I'm especially pleased to see that it's a northern lad who has triumphed!"

Inside pages:
- Full match report and more photographs
- 'Mum's Yorkshire puds built me up'

CULL VALLEY EVENING GAZETTE

Tuesday September 1 2009

Three killed in horror smash

Blackspot claims more lives
by Jeannie Derby

Three people were killed instantly when a car smashed through the safety barrier at a notorious bend on a Cull Valley road yesterday.

An eyewitness said that the driver, 32-year-old Mrs Julia Yates, of Green Pastures, Hexroyd, appeared to have lost control of the vehicle, which plunged down an embankment and burst into flames.

With Mrs Yates in the car were her 40-year-old husband Anthony Yates, the architect and newly-elected chairman of the Mid-Pennine Chamber of Commerce, and Edward Beresford, 34, until recently a *Cull Valley Evening Gazette* journalist.

Road-safety pressure groups have long campaigned for new barriers and speed restrictions on the A8814 between Ainsley and Hexroyd. The crash was the third fatal incident at the spot this year.

Farmer Thomas Heslop was driving his tractor close to the scene when Mrs Yates left the road.

He said: "I must have been a good 100 yards away but I heard this terrible noise, like a rhythmic metallic banging. I turned and saw one of those Harry Potter cars, you know, an old Ford Anglia, tip over the barrier. It seemed to hover in mid-air and then, just for a moment, I thought it was on fire. I think the sun must have caught the red bodywork. The car turned over and landed on its roof. Then it really did burst into flames."

Friends and colleagues here at the *Gazette* paid their own tribute with a minute's silence on the editorial floor. Mrs Hazel Moses, the women's page editor, said: "Teddy, as he liked to be known, was a fine writer and sub-editor. He was a journalist to his bones and was a real credit to our profession. Many people remember with affection his occasional column, *Beresford's Beat*, which was just before my time here. It could be quirky, angry or rather dark, sometimes all three at once.

"Teddy was good fun to work with and, most importantly, my husband Jim and I will remember him as a great friend."

A spokesman at Josh Yates Builders, the family firm where church warden Mr Yates was a director, said that that they were "devastated" by the loss.

Mr and Mrs Yates had been married for eight years. They had no children. Mr Beresford, who was single, lived in Ainsley with his parents, Dr Philip and Dr Valerie Beresford.

Hazel Moses' tribute to Teddy Beresford: Page 6

Stories they cannot print

JEANNIE DERBY....

This has been the unhappiest day of my life, writing about the death of my friends Teddy and Anthony. I was in a very emotional state; I don't think, had my head been clearer, that I would have included the farmer's reference to Harry Potter, which sounded almost whimsical.

I was never a pal of Anthony, somewhere between friend and acquaintance you could say. I don't think anyone ever got truly close to him. But after meeting through St Luke's Church, we enjoyed some interesting conversations about life, work and faith, even though I was never convinced that his heart was in the right place.

And things did not go too well on our first meeting. Anthony wasn't thrilled when I was appointed a church warden; goodness knows how he would react if the church ever appointed a female vicar.....goodness knows, I should say, how he would have reacted. But he was impressed with my commitment to the church and he wasn't a man who was put off by my appearance.

Because, to put it bluntly, I am plain. Men bring this home to me regularly in all sorts of ways, some more subtle than others. A few chaps don't see me at all; I am the invisible woman. Others go for pity, tilting their head ever so slightly sideways, like an over-solicitous primary school teacher, as they talk to me. Some men assume wrongly that their comments go over my head. When I was introduced to everybody on my first day at the Gazette, the deputy sports editor nudged his boss and hissed the name of a goofy, long-faced Newcastle footballer from the 1970s. My father's a Magpies' fan, so I've seen the player on some kind of 'golden goals' DVD; the similarity did not escape me. At least it's a long time since I had any in-your-face insults, unless you count last year's Christmas party.

Kenneth Thrower, our loving and esteemed deputy editor, got so spectacularly drunk that, after gawping intently for about 30 seconds, he said: "Christ, Jeannie, you aren't half ugly." I half-expected an apology the following Monday but Thrower's behaviour towards me was unchanged. I knew he had forgotten the incident. For me it made no odds, I already had him down as someone who wasn't quite as nice as he thought he was.

Mark McClair, our dearest and no-less-loving Editor (never forget the capped 'E'), is marginally more subtle. I know this because Thrower passes on His Master's Messages in a manner exemplary for its accuracy: "The boss wonders if a photo-led feature on speed-dating is really playing to your strengths, Jeannie. Perhaps we could find someone else?"

Circumstances which I shudder to think about now brought Teddy and me closer although as a hands-on God botherer, I was never going to be on his wavelength quite in the way that my colleagues Stan Cartwright and Hazel Moses were. Then again, maybe I'm underselling myself; because during the last year or so I've developed a distinct impression that Teddy saw me as a potential, personal agony aunt. He used to come over all serious and say to me: "You know, Jeannie..." then tail off, as if he had thought better of it, because my faith might make me censorious in my judgments.

When I put this to Stan, I expected him to laugh it off, or to give me one of his quizzical, John Le Mesurier-style raised eyebrows, indicating that I was being just a trifle fanciful. Instead, he said: "I'm in the same boat, listening to tales of his lost loves and squandered opportunities, all for the price of a pint."

A few months ago, I would have counted Teddy as one of the most pleasant men I'd ever met: unaffected, modest, a good listener. Well, I still think that way, although I was disappointed when I found out about his relationship with Julia Yates. What was Teddy thinking about, getting involved with Julia, the vainest, most self-regarding and self-centred individual I've ever met?

Okay, I'm not stupid. I can see what the attraction was for men. But somehow I imagined Teddy to be above that sort of thing. Wrongly, it seems.

But on balance, I'm sure that Heaven is his destination.

CULL VALLEY EVENING GAZETTE

Tuesday September 1 2009 (From front page)

My friend, Teddy

Women's page editor Hazel Moses pays tribute to her former *Gazette* colleague, Edward 'Teddy' Beresford, who has died in a car crash

I am numb with shock following the death of my great friend Teddy Beresford in the tragic accident that claimed three lives.

I moved here in 2006 from north London, as a news reporter. When I joined the sub-editors' desk later that year, I found myself sitting next to Teddy. We discovered immediately a similar sense of humour, and we had great fun bouncing ideas for good headlines off one another. There were times when the chief sub-editor considered splitting us up because we were like a couple of noisy school kids!

Teddy was a great all-rounder as a journalist, equally comfortable as a news reporter, features writer, columnist or sub-editor. He certainly had some illuminating and offbeat views, which he explored when he was a columnist with the *Gazette*.

In spite of that, Teddy worked to live rather than the other way round. And it's as a friend that I will remember him, with that offbeat sense of humour and ready smile. After I met my husband-to-be, Jim, we used to get together as a foursome with Teddy's girlfriend of the moment. He had a great knack of getting on with people, perhaps helped by a wide range of sporting and cultural interests that enabled him to relate to everybody.

Someone once suggested to me that Teddy didn't suffer fools gladly. However, that was never the case. He was actually very tolerant of human frailties, some of which he cheerfully admitted to himself. It was more – and his friends admired him for it – a reluctance to engage with the occasional sycophants and dissemblers who crossed his path. This is a quality which you don't come across everywhere, and which I found truly refreshing in him.

My heart goes out to Philip and Val, Teddy's lovely parents, who were so welcoming to Jim and me.

Goodbye and God Bless, Teddy, we'll never forget you.

Stories they cannot print

HAZEL MOSES....

The most awful thing is that we thought we'd lost Teddy last year. I still find it hard to talk about what happened then; or to handle having become, together with Jeannie, some kind of saint in the eyes of his parents.

The office gossips speculated about Teddy and me, encouraged by some nudge-nudge wink-wink from Thrower and Jekyll; they'd sussed that I carried ever so briefly a torch for Teddy. It took three post-work trips to the pub to work out that I was wasting my time. After a few beers Teddy would make wistful references to former girlfriends – he just couldn't help himself – in a way that you wouldn't if you had the faintest interest in someone. I'm very precise about the moment the penny dropped because our teacher at my creative writing class had been talking about use of the 'magic three': the third occasion something happens being the moment in drama and comedy when revelations are made, or jokes are revealed. I couldn't help laughing when Teddy recalled an old flame and I realised it had taken me three evenings to twig his indifference to me as anything other than a friend.

"What's so funny?" Teddy, unable to see anything amusing in the conversation, had asked me.

"Wouldn't really translate," I said. "It was to do with my writing class at the tech."

"What sort of stuff do you write?"

"Nothing too serious, I know my limitations. Romantic fiction, I suppose you might call it chick lit. Maybe I've missed the boat for that kind of thing. It was all the rage a few years ago, though I'm still trying."

"Keep at it if you enjoy it," said Teddy.

"You ever thought of writing a novel yourself, Teddy? I guess all of us journos play with the idea at some point."

"I suppose we do," he said, "I'm absolutely convinced that this dead friend of mine, Henry Hawley, would have made a real name for himself. Not that he was actually a journalist, he'd dabbled in our trade but he was aiming for academia."

"What about you?" I said, making a mental note that I ought to ask about Henry.

"I don't really think so," he said, tearing a Cockcroft's Golden Accelerator beer mat into neat strips. "I've always thought that it's too much of a busman's holiday."

"If you're not going to use your escapades yourself, perhaps I could make them material for my humble efforts," I said light-heartedly.

"Perhaps you could, feel free," he said, without much apparent enthusiasm.

Then I did ask Teddy to tell me about Henry Hawley, and he perked up. It struck me even at that early stage of our friendship that I'd hit on one of the many contradictions in Teddy's personality. He could be excessively self-absorbed, but he had a higher regard for the talents of others than he had for anything to do with himself.

CULL VALLEY EVENING GAZETTE

Wednesday November 12 2008

Strike gave me a lucky break

It's National Local Newspapers' Week (NLNW), when the industry celebrates the vibrancy of Britain's regional press. Teddy Beresford, one of our senior journalists, explains how he joined the profession

I had a couple of obsessions as a youngster: to win the singles title at Wimbledon and to be a sports journalist when my playing days were over. I combined these two wishes by making up stories about my grand-slam triumphs for the sports pages of a little paper which I called the *National Diary*.

My mother once took a set off Virginia Wade at a pre-Wimbledon tournament in Manchester. In my mid-teens, Mum broke it to me, as gently as possible, that my lack of a competitive streak made it unlikely I'd get much further than county seconds' standard. In any case, I only grew to five foot seven, very small for a tennis player these days. So it had to be journalism all the way!

I contributed to Devon University's student newspaper throughout my three years as an undergraduate. Helping to expose a scam perpetrated by the rag committee taught me something positive about the power of the press. At Easter, before my final term in 1996, I came in to this newspaper's front office to point out an inaccuracy in an *Evening Gazette* article.

By chance, the then news editor Stan Cartwright – now a good friend and colleague of mine – was at the front counter. He said: "Well, why don't you come in for a week before you go back to university and see if you can do any better?"

It's funny the little things that can map out our entire future. On the Monday, I made a mediocre fist of a few small jobs. The following morning, two reporters went off sick. Stan, against his better judgment, sent me out to cover a couple's golden wedding on my own. He gave me an idiot's guide of things to ask: Where did you meet, where did you go for your honeymoon, what did you do for a living, what's the secret of a happy married life, that kind of thing. "By the way," he added. "Don't hang around too long with the coffee and biscuits, some of these old folks will be happy to talk all day to a personable young lad like you. We'll need the editorial car for other jobs." He didn't say "bigger jobs". Stan treated every story in the paper very seriously, and understood that everything was important to the people we were writing about.

I remember being nervous at suddenly having this responsibility thrust on me; a real interview, a real story and a car I'd never driven before. But I had a cheery encounter in the *Gazette* car park with the sports editor, Jim Stafford, who now works in Birmingham.

Jim was a hero of mine, thanks to his brilliant, highly animated coverage of Hexroyd Park Avenue in my teenage years, when the club reached two FA Cup quarter-finals. So when he said: "You'll be fine, mate, it's not rocket science," it fair put a spring in my step!

It was one of the coldest April days on record and I noticed that these men outside a dairy were standing around a brazier, and holding placards. *Why are they doing that? Is it a story?* I hadn't yet entered the mobile-phone era so I couldn't contact Stan. I thought about his come-back-soon warning, then decided that he could hardly fire a one-week work experience person earning nothing apart from a couple of free pints, so I stopped to find out what it was all about.

"Blimey, where have you been?" said Stan, when I finally returned. "Second helping of Jaffa cakes irresistible?"

It was a strike and no one had tipped off the paper. I wrote it up with a little help on house style from Stan. The sub-editor dealing with my piece (they're the people responsible for writing headlines, designing the pages, checking copy for style and accuracy and generally making everything fit) didn't want to give "a work experience boy", as I recall it was phrased by the user, a by-line. But Stan pulled rank and there it was, the splash, as we journalists call the day's biggest, front-page story: "Thirty out in tea-break strike", by Edward Beresford. "Row over brew time brings dairy to its knees."

On my last day, Stan took me for lunch and told me to keep in touch. After doing a postgraduate journalism course in Cardiff, I got my job with the *Gazette*. That was 11 years ago and I've been here ever since, first as a trainee, then a fully-fledged reporter and now I'm a sub-editor myself.

I've loved every minute. One or two colleagues have moved on to so-called bigger things, such as national papers, TV, radio or well-paid public relations work, the 'dark side' as some of us like to call it.

But I love working on my own patch, for a newspaper which is truly at the heart of the local community. Because that's what the regional press is all about.

Stories they cannot print

TEDDY BERESFORD....

Our editor, Mark McClair, was happy enough with that spiel. It appealed less to my immediate boss, Frances 'Doc' (inevitably) Jekyll, the sub-editor who'd felt I shouldn't have been given a by-line because I was a "work experience boy"; she thought I was having a dig at her, and she was right. Frances might look shambolic, a shapeless, blotchy-faced 45-year-old from whom youth's bloom has long departed, but she is street-wise and devious, perfectly capable of working out that "as I recall it was phrased by the user" was an over-elaborate way of preserving her anonymity; the personal pronoun would have given her away. And someone, Thrower or McClair perhaps, managed to make his own, special thumb print on the article by slipping in 'then' before Stan Cartwright's job title.

Stan, who mock-vomited after reading the final paragraph, is a great buddy and we've had some fine, drink-fuelled evenings together. For a chap in his 50s he can't half shift the ale. My dad, who's 63, says: "When I was his age, I was down to two and a half pints an evening." On our nights out, I've told Stan things that I wish I'd kept to myself; he probably knows more about me than even my closest friends, Rory and Ruth Nolan. "So I'm back in the psychiatrist's chair," he says tolerantly, when he has to listen as I explore the deepest recesses of my own mind.

Stan and I often have a laugh about our first meeting. It was the day of my 21st birthday and I was having a lunchtime pint with two old school friends, Henry 'Hank' (because he liked country music) Hawley and Paul 'Paolo' (because his mother was Italian) Hopkinson. My best pal Henry, just home from six months in Caen, was leafing through that day's Cull Valley Evening Gazette.

"Have a look at this, Teddy."

"Nice to see the old town hasn't forgotten you," added Paul.

'Auntie Jean sends her warmest greetings to this week's Gazette Birthday Club Boys and Girls. They are:

Nancy Sydenham (7)
Paul Rhodes (9)

Stephen Crowther (6)
Marcus Godfrey (11)
David Tysall (10)
Edward Beresford (21)
Ricky Foster (10)
Joe and Alfie Sinclair (twins), (4)
Janice Olsen (8)
Tanya Greenwood (12)
Ephraim (Fima) Lazarus (12)

Happy Birthday, boys and girls!'

What followed at the hands of Hank and Paolo would have been described by professional footballers as "a ribbing off the lads". The alcohol induced a sense-of-humour failure, and I headed for the Gazette office brandishing the paper.

Funny to think that if the article had appeared today, I couldn't have complained in person without getting on a bus; Hank and Paolo would have persuaded me to laugh it off, end of story.

But in my university days, the paper was still in the centre of Hexroyd. The three-storey red-brick Victorian building had a mustiness and faded glory more suited to the vanished world of typewriters, chain-smoking and hard-core drinking than the new era of PCs, Apple Macs and snatched lunches from the trolley. As staffing levels plummeted, and the presses disappeared altogether (the Gazette is now printed elsewhere) we were increasingly rattling round in an absurdly large space. The paper moved three years ago and we are now in Anytown UK, just off the northern ring road and equidistant from Hexroyd and Ainsley. Our nearest neighbour, and architectural soul mate, is a massive supermarket, next to which we look like an afterthought, as if Tesco had added on a house-and-home section later. Only the cheap and gaudy yellow lettering, Cull Valley Evening Gazette, deters shoppers from a wrong turning. The River Cull runs close by, flanked by graffiti-sprayed advertising billboards, a tiles showroom and two automobile dealerships. Both forecourts have spiral stands showing off the latest sports model, raised high above the ground so that the car sits at a rakish angle, like an aircraft. This annoys me; jet planes are entitled to do that, motor cars aren't.

Staff with time to stray beyond the trolley can dine at the Burgers 4 All bar, a charmless franchise operation on the site of Neptunes, a long-demolished fish and chip restaurant where I was brought for a meal to celebrate passing my West Pennine Grammar entrance exam. The chippie's glossy blue-green walls in mock-pine cladding were dotted with comic-book fish, watched over by a benevolent, winking octopus. It looked like the sea god's grotto from a church panto. In the corner, someone had painted a grinning salmon, tucking into fish and chips wrapped in newspaper. As a child, I found this merry cannibalism faintly off-putting but now, seeing the plastic, greasy frontage of Burgers 4 All on my way into work, I feel almost wistful about the Cull Valley's lost "number one fish and chip supper venue".

Back in 1996, I was able to take my Birthday Club grumble into the Evening Gazette office on foot. A middle-aged guy with thinning hair and the beginnings of a beer belly was having a laugh with the woman on reception, presenting her with a big red book, as if it were This is Your Life. "DAR-da-da-DAAAR. Tonight, Jolene Dickinson..."

"Pardon me interrupting the fun. It's to do with your birthday column," I said.

"Oh dear, you've not come about Tanya Greenwood, have you?" he said, looking anxiously at his book, which had the words "Gazette Birthday Club" in large print, taped across the front.

"No. What's up with Tanya?"

"We've shamed and defamed her. She's 12, two years too old for a name check from Auntie Jean."

"In that case, same applies to the Lazarus boy, doesn't it?" I put the Gazette down on the counter and prodded young Ephraim's name three times with my index finger. "Also 12 years old, it says here."

"Fair question but Fima will be fine, he lives in Hexroyd. Tanya's an Ainsley lass."

"And what's six miles of the A8814 got to do with some kids being more red-faced than others?"

"Another reasonable question, perhaps you should join our trade. Kids in Ainsley are more street wise. It's something to do with the number of 'off-comers' and the one-parent families, it turns the boys into little emperors. So we're supposed to remove them from the Birthday Club when they reach ten, but Hexroyd kids stay on until 12."

"In other words, everyone's out of your big red book by the time they're teenagers, even the non-sophisticates of Hexroyd," I said, seizing the opportunity to play the prosecuting lawyer catching out a witness.

"Of course."

"But not this Beresford guy," I said. "Me."

"Blimey," he said, looking at the paper. I could see that he was struggling to keep a straight face. "I'm really sorry about that."

He opened the book at March 30, and there I was: 'Edward Beresford, Geneva Row, Ainsley, born 1975'. At some point in the past my name had been crossed out, but not very decisively.

"Even so," I said, beginning to see the funny side, "a bit of common sense might have told the compiler to take me out. It's a schoolboy error."

"You're absolutely right, that's exactly what it is." he said. "This sort of thing often happens when we get GCSE kids here on work experience. The lad who did this seems pretty much incapable of stringing a sentence together. Though his teacher tells me he's in some sort of gifted category. Does make you wonder about the rest of them."

"Well, I'm sure I could improve on that. I was part of the University of Devon team who uncovered the rag committee charity scam, you know. It made a few paragraphs in a couple of the nationals," I said airily, trying to sound like a journalist.

"Yes, I remember reading something. I tell you what, oh and by the way I'm Stan Cartwright, the news editor," he said holding out his hand for me to shake, "Why don't you come in for a week and see if you can do any better, before you go back to university? You can go out on a few jobs with reporters and knock some press releases into shape. You could help out with one or two advertisement features, come to think of it."

"What are they?"

"You know, for the advertisers, the generic stuff. Time to book your holidays, Shopping in Hexroyd, Get a dog for Christmas, that sort of thing."

"Funny," I said, "I'd never really thought of anyone writing all that."

"Wrong way round, Edward. The stuff has to be written, but nobody ever reads it. You can say pretty much what you like, as long as it's not positively libellous. Reckon you're up to that?"

"I think so."

"No money I'm afraid, although I'm sure I'll be able to run to the odd pint. You're clearly a man who likes a drink. Five days starting on Monday? Nine o'clock sharp at this desk."

"Great, thanks very much, Mr Cartwright."

The National Diary

June 2008

'All About Me'

Teddy Beresford, aged 33, is a sub-editor on the *Cull Valley Evening Gazette*, the daily newspaper where he has worked since he graduated in English Literature from the University of Devon. He is the only child of two doctors. His mother, Dr Valerie Beresford, is the *Gazette*'s anonymous agony aunt

When were you happiest?
The day Rachel Waterfall first smiled at me, shortly after she arrived in the Cull Valley from Devon.

What is your greatest regret?
Losing my rag on match point in the Hexroyd Tennis Club U18 final – and then retreating into my shell after the event. I spent what should have been the most important evening of my life replaying the whole thing endlessly in my mind and writing it up as a report for the *National Diary*. (See below: What did you want to be?)

What is your greatest fear?
Dying young. I attempted suicide a few months ago and, as the last few pills went down, I understood the distress my actions would cause those closest to me.

Worst of times?
See above, but also when my friend Henry 'Hank' Hawley died of cancer, aged 23. As I lay there – so I thought – dying, I recalled Hank's bravery, and reflected on my cowardice.

With which historical figure do you most identify?
Anyone who's ever snatched defeat from the jaws of victory.

Who would you like to be if you could come back as anyone?
Tom Waterfall – that's Tom Hogg as was.

What would your motto be?
Carpe diem – because I didn't.

Who are the most important people in your life?
My mum and dad, Valerie and Philip, and my best friends, Rory and Ruth Nolan.

What is your favourite novel?
The Unconsoled, by Kazuo Ishiguro.

What is your favourite film?
I still love the French New Wave. It would have to be a toss-up between *The 400 Blows*, and *Jules and Jim*.

What is your favourite painting?
The Day of Atonement, by Jacob Kramer.

What is your favourite music?
Late Beatles, the White Album takes some beating.

What did you want to be when you grew up?
A tennis player and a journalist. As a youngster, I used to write for my own newspaper, the *National Diary*. There would be features, columns, even short stories. I was quite an imaginative kid. I say 'used to write' but that's not the case. As you can see, the *National Diary* is still going strong. In my teens and early 20s, I continued to write things up, as the mood took me, and then filed them away. A few years ago, I started transferring everything to my PC, resisting the temptation to airbrush here and there, or to put a more comfortable sheen on my, shall we say, less distinguished moments. The *Diary* has continued to be a useful way to examine what's happening around me.

Isn't that weird?
Well, just a little maybe. Then again, lots of people keep diaries and they all have different ways of going about it. This is my way, through newspaper articles, and it's an opportunity to be creative

and get into other people's heads. For example, to look at the way I might appear to my mother, or to one of my friends.

It's a bit presumptuous, surely, to assume that you can know how other people's minds work?

Isn't that what novelists do all the time? Although, yes, I accept that occasionally it would be a nigh impossible task. I once had the idea of writing up my relationship with a girlfriend through her eyes. I decided that it could be done through *Bridget Jones's Diary*-style extracts. In the end, the concept proved too ambitious; I would have had to alter her perspective slightly with every entry, to reflect her changing perceptions of me. And one or two of my old flames are so unknowable that I wouldn't know where to begin. You'd have to get it from the horse's mouth.

You mentioned your late friend Henry Hawley earlier. Does the *National Diary* give you, in some curious way, a chance to *be* him?

That's absolutely correct. I imagine the projects in which Henry might have involved himself, as a newspaper columnist and book writer. I think about him every day and I will always miss him, a part of me died with him. It's a funny thing, but writing as Henry keeps him alive for me and brings me a strange sense of comfort.

Moving on, who is your favourite artist?
Matisse.

What is your favourite possession?
My complete set of Beatles' records, on vinyl, all the original pressings. A present from my parents on my 18th birthday.

What words or expressions do you most overuse?
Would she have been happy with me?

How would you like to die?
Peacefully, as an old man, surrounded by friends and maybe family, remembering only the good things in my life.

What do you consider your greatest achievement?
None.

Which sports teams team do you support?
For football, it's Hexroyd Park Avenue even though I live in
Ainsley. Avenue has always been my mum's team. We finished
seventh in League One (the third tier of professional football) last
season, just missing the play-offs, so we're punching above our
weight right now. But I've always had a soft spot for Ainsley
Athletic because Barry, our old window cleaner, used to play for
them.

For rugby, it's West Yorks Wasps. One of my earliest memories is
being taken by Mum to watch Dad playing at scrum-half, at the end
of his playing career. The three of us still go to the Wasps' home
games together. I've always been more of a rugby union man,
although I'd occasionally go with Hank to Hexroyd Hornets rugby
league.

I'm Yorkshire through and through for cricket, obviously!

Can you tell us something surprising?
I prefer tall women. All other things being equal, I just find them
physically more attractive. Perhaps it's an inherited characteristic
from my father, as Mum's four inches taller than he is. As my
parents have got older, they've begun to look like an ever-odder
pairing: Dad sports an untidy beard and, with his rugby-playing days
long behind him, has become rather stout, while Mum is slim, silver
haired and elegant, like a model in a Saga holiday brochure.

Who would play you in the film of your life?
John Simm.

What is your most realistic potential achievement?
I'd like to be a dad one day. If I never find the right woman,
perhaps I could at least be a sperm donor. Do they still take the stuff
at my age? Maybe I need to get on with it.

Julia's Journal

Well, who'd have thought it? I do believe that I might have found him at last. He's called Teddy Beresford and he came into the shop the other day when thoughts of love could not have been further from my mind.

No, let's be absolutely honest, here, Lady. Otherwise there's no point chronicling your efforts to pin down Mr Right. I *was* actually thinking about men. Spit it out, I was thinking about that Robbie Santiago and what a bastard he turned out to be. Anthony thinks he's a Chav, and he's right.

But Robbie was only a fling. Teddy could be the real deal. He's obviously very clever, and honest as the day is long. Well, quite preposterously honest. Would I have acted like he did in the shop the other day? Not on your Nelly!

It turns out that the Cull Valley Gazette is going to carry an article about Teddy's good deed. I hope they use the bit I told the reporter, it might encourage him to come in again. Perhaps, when I said to Teddy: "It's a pity you're not here every day!" that gave him encouragement enough!

The one disappointing feature of the whole business is that our manager, Cath Wilson, thinks Teddy works on the local rag himself. But Cath does know for sure that he's the son of the Beresford doctors. They won't be poor, will they?

Anyway, Lady, early days. More inquiries are needed

CULL VALLEY EVENING GAZETTE

Tuesday December 9 2008

Honest Teddy goes by the book

Rare Greene novel puts charity shop staff in the pink
By Gavin Layton

Cull Valley Evening Gazette journalist Teddy Beresford created the news himself when he spent a morning browsing in a charity shop.

Teddy, 33, spotted a valuable book on the shelves of Ainsley Battling Cancer (ABC). Graham Greene's first novel, *The Man Within*, was selling for £1.50, but the 1929 first edition is now so rare that copies have changed hands for more than £1,000. Teddy pointed this out to astonished shop manager Cath Wilson, and the book will now be sold through an auction house, in all probability for a four-figure sum.

Cath said: "We can't be experts on everything here, and things like this do slip through our fingers from time to time. One current ABC project is to raise funds for a bus which will take cancer patients door-to-door for specialist treatment in Leeds. The dream is now, thanks to Teddy, that much nearer to being turned into a reality."

And shop assistant Mrs Julia Yates said simply: "Teddy is our hero! It's a wonderful, wonderful gesture."

Bibliophile Beresford admits to 'dabbling' in a bit of buying and selling of old books – but says that the modern first edition is an area he has only begun to explore recently.

He adds modestly: "I could hardly have failed to spot this book as I'm a fan of Graham Greene and knew that his first novel was published originally in a very small edition, and is therefore extremely rare. What's really incredible is to find one with the original dust jacket, and in such good condition, too.

"I'm especially delighted that a cancer charity will benefit. One of my closest friends died of leukaemia when he was just 23."

There's another happy spin-off to Teddy's discovery. In the New Year, he has offered to come into the shop once a month, to sift through new stock, advise on pricing and alert staff to the presence of any books which are potentially valuable.

And does this mean that we should all be checking our shelves for valuable items?

Teddy explains: "There's no harm in looking, although you will probably be disappointed. In the end it's all about rarity. *Most* books are first editions simply because no one wanted a second edition. Early books by famous writers are often worth the most because when they started out no one could possibly have known how they would take off. So if anyone's got an unwanted first edition of *Watership Down*, or *Harry Potter and the Philosopher's Stone*, I'd be happy to take it off their hands!"

Stories they cannot print

GAVIN LAYTON.....

That was nice work by Teddy. He's a good bloke, you can always rely on him to do the right thing. When I turned up here with my Oxford degree in Oriental Studies, there were a few people who wanted to put me in my place. You know what I mean: "Welcome to the real world, pal."

But not Teddy. He was incredibly helpful in ironing out a few small details that I kept getting wrong in my reports for the paper; as well as some less minor things such as burying significant details near the bottom of the story. "Don't you think the readers might want to know more about this? What I'd suggest is...." he'd say, in his mild-mannered way.

I often run ideas past him first, rather than going to that sarcastic twat Kenneth 'Chuck' Thrower, our deputy editor, who loves coming down like a ton of bricks on my copy. "There's taxis, and then there's private-hire cabs. Not the same fucking thing at all. But I don't suppose you learned about that when you were looking at irregular Turkish verbs," he said on one occasion. "I didn't do Turkish, and, in any case, it only has one irregular verb," I replied, inadvisedly.

I'm a quick learner, though I say it myself, and once it became clear that I knew what I was doing, Teddy had some advice.

"There are worse places to work than this, despite your McClairs and Throwers, but don't stay here for ever. You've no ties and you don't want to end up like me and Stan Cartwright."

"Well, Stan Cartwright, maybe not...," I said, raising my eyebrows and aiming for a sympathy-pity combo. "But you, your job's okay and you've not exactly got one foot in the grave. You could even branch out and go into something completely different."

"Even so," Teddy said, as if my suggestion had barely registered, "I just get the feeling that things are slipping away from me a little."

I know that Teddy's suffered from depression, and he was in a particularly low mood the morning I was told to interview him for the charity shop story. I walked across to his desk and had some difficulty getting him to concentrate on the matter in hand.

"Look at this, Gav," he said, nodding in the direction of the news desk. Our office is open plan, which provides ample opportunity for

distraction. All the time there are little cameos being played out across the floor. Thrower was trying to amuse a young advertising girl in a low-cut dress; Teddy and I were impressed with the way he almost succeeded in keeping his eyes off her cleavage.

"I sometimes think that I should be putting back more in my free time," said Teddy when I brought him round to the subject of his rare book find. "My parents have always been involved in loads of interests and projects. A little charity work wouldn't go amiss; maybe I could start by lending Ainsley Battling Cancer a hand. You know, digging out some of the more valuable books that are brought in, like the one I found, so they don't go for a song."

"Julia Yates would be thrilled, Teddy."

"Sorry?"

"The blonde, she really fell for you hook, line and sinker."

"You think so?" said Teddy, smiling for the first time that morning.

"I know so. 'Teddy is our hero' is quite clear-cut. Can I add it to the story?"

"You mean, 'My hots for local journalist', by charity shop babe'?" he said. You always knew Teddy was cheering up when he started becoming facetious.

"That, of course," I deadpanned, "But I also meant the bit about your helping out at the shop."

"Yeah, Gavin, why not. I'll give Cath Wilson a call, and tell her my services are at her disposal."

"You're not going to pursue her, are you?" I said. "Julia, I mean. Story is, from someone at the Chamber of Commerce, that she was a lavender bride and that the architect husband's tastes lie elsewhere. And you must have heard the rumours about Julia and Chuck Thrower?"

"Thrower?" Teddy said. "Is she mental?"

But I could tell by the way Teddy smiled to himself that he thought Thrower's would be an easy challenge to overcome. He was slipping off into another reverie, and I decided to leave him to it.

The National Diary

January 2009

'Sexy education' provided lessons for life

Henry Hawley goes back to school

Last night, I dreamt I went to West Pennine Grammar again. It was one of Greasy Gillespie's long and dusty Friday afternoon classes in early June. The exams were over, and summer was just around the corner. I was sitting next to my old school chum Teddy Beresford, currently working on the sub-editors' desk at the *Cull Valley Gazette* in West Yorkshire. (He favoured Teddy over Ted or Edward because he thought it made him sound like a Battle of Britain fighter pilot).

It was Teddy who whispered those immortal words to me – in 1992, it must have been – during Gillespie's French class. "The trouble with Greasy," said Teddy, "is that, okay, he gets results, but he's just not cool enough. What we really need – and one day it will come, too late for us – is sexy education."

No one could reasonably have taken issue with this assessment of the school's expert on Racine and Balzac. Even, I suspect, Mrs Gillespie. Greasy's nickname was ironic; he was a flaky individual with enough dandruff on his jacket shoulders to feed a family of cockroaches for a fortnight. But what occurs to me now is that Teddy has surely secured a place in the *Oxford English Dictionary*. He must have been the first person to use the word 'sexy' in this fashion, meaning thrilling, pulsating, life-enhancing, as in Ruud Gullit's demand for 'sexy football'.

As for the education prediction, we all thought Teddy was whistling in the dark. But how wrong we were, and how galling it is that our old rivals Hexroyd Grammar School now sit atop the Government's recently published League Table of the Sexiest Schools. We West Pennine boys used to be close rivals to the lads at HGS but, since the introduction of the Independent Schools' Sexy Super League, a few big spenders have pulled so far ahead of the pack that the rest are nowhere, and it's impossible to see them ever catching up.

It's common knowledge now that a handful of these schools are paying huge sums for the best teachers from around the world. As a result, the brightest kids won't go anywhere else and so the cycle continues. And *every* kid of school age wants to be associated with Hexroyd, Manchester or Bradford Grammar. Visit any town or city in the country this summer and you'll see youngsters going round wearing HGS uniforms. Most of these kids have never even set foot in Hexroyd. Any true Hexroydians will tell you that West Pennine GS will always be the genuine school for locals.

There's another price to pay for the sexy education revolution. It's the grotesquely inflated salaries that some of these teachers now command. Schools like Manchester, Bradford and HGS can carry a few mistakes. If the modern languages department at HGS takes on a young Bavarian teacher, and he fails to reproduce the black-board skills he showed at a Munich gymnasium, he can be offloaded during the half-term transfer window with a shrug. The West Pennine Grammars of this world can't afford to do this; if a foreign teacher on hefty wages doesn't deliver, they're in trouble.

There will always be fair-weather performers among our imports, especially from South America and Africa. If you put a Colombian or Nigerian teacher in our classrooms in September, when gentle, late summer sunshine filters through the windows, they are fine. But come December and January, when there's ice on the ground and the school's central heating system is on the blink, many of them don't want to know. Some of these mercenaries are happy to pick up £50,000 a week for supervising free periods.

As for the home-grown talent, the Greasy Gillespies of this world, unable to break into the Independent School first teams and relegated to inner-city comprehensives, they are being thrown into the dustbin of history.

One of my new year's resolutions was to look up a few folk I've not seen for a while. I really should contact old Teddy Beresford. We could maybe go together to a match at Hexroyd Park Avenue, like we did in the old days. It would be good to find out what he makes of it all. We've got our sexy education now, Teddy. But at what price?

- Henry Hawley's first novel, Quintessence of Dust (Idlewild, £7.99), will be published on January 26

CULL VALLEY EVENING GAZETTE

Monday January 12 2009

That was the day we met...

There are plenty of 'Happy Ever Afters' – just read our touching golden and diamond weddings stories. Hazel Moses begins a new weekly feature on first encounters by talking to Rory and Ruth Nolan

There's an element of telepathy among many couples in long-established relationships.

You can see it when you talk to book-binders Rory and Ruth Nolan: in the way that they gently interrupt one another, or finish each other's sentences.

The remarkable thing about Rory and Ruth, however, is that the telepathy has existed since the moment they met.

"Something just clicked, and I think that we both knew it straightaway. We just tuned right into one another. We met at a student party, about half way through our first term at Devon University," Ruth recalls, and they both grin broadly at the memory. "Rory just swept me off my feet, although he always laughs when I tell him that. You see, he wasn't very confident when it came to chatting up girls, and the way he was trying so hard with me, well, it was really endearing."

"We were both 19 and Ruth was my first serious girlfriend," says Rory, who has inherited the trace of a gentle Irish accent from his father. "I thought she looked just perfect, and I was determined to chat her up. But it wasn't that easy for me, you know, Hazel, I've always been quite shy. I'd also seen her around the campus with another lad, so I thought she had a steady boyfriend already."

The bit about shyness certainly came as a surprise to me. Rory, with his firm handshake, broad shoulders, jet-black hair and piercing blue eyes, struck me as a real charmer when he greeted me at their delightful eighteenth century converted barn outside Hexroyd, overlooking the moors. I paused for a second while I took in both the view and his words.

"I know, it's surprising isn't it?" says Ruth, apparently extending her telepathic skills to me. "I'm the extrovert one, really."

Ruth, who combines book-binding with supply work as a teacher of history and English, is a real girl-next-door type, the sort of lass whose looks grow on the boys as they begin to appreciate her warm personality and infectious sense of humour. Unless, of course, those boys have the perspicacity of someone like Rory, who gets the full picture right away.

Rory and Ruth have been together since that day, and there's a rather charming postscript to the story. The "other lad" Rory had seen with Ruth was my colleague at the *Evening Gazette*, Teddy Beresford. He had been Ruth's first boyfriend at college but is now the closest friend of the Nolans. And when Rory and Ruth finally tied the knot, Teddy was the best man.

The couple continue to sing from the same hymn sheet, and love working together as book-binders.

Are they going to live happily ever after? You bet they are!

It's love that makes the world go round and the couples I'll be talking to during the next few weeks, some young like Rory and Ruth, and one or two much older, will be making that very point for me!

STORIES....HAZEL MOSES.....

I had Kenneth Thrower, our delightful deputy editor, in my face today.

"You could and should have made more of that. What about the book-binding? Interesting job, I would have thought. And how do they get on working together, as well as living together?"

"It did occur to me," I improvised, "but then I figured that could be the subject of an altogether different feature on another occasion. Family business partnerships, perhaps?"

I'm not great at thinking on my feet, so I reckon that was pretty good by my standards. Thrower was right, of course, although he could have put it less aggressively.

"Okay, then," he said, "Keep me posted."

I'd lost sight of that angle, maybe because I'd spent too much time dwelling on something Ruth said to me, and whether or not to include it.

What I'd written originally, to conclude my piece, was: "It's now six years since the couple tied the knot and Rory and Ruth, both 34, have recently had the best gift of all. They've learned that Ruth is finally going to be a mum.

"It really is a miracle," says Ruth. "We just thought it was never going to happen for us."

She was beside herself, but I wondered if joy had briefly clouded her judgment, and that we were going into print too soon with this happy news. Isn't three months common practice before an announcement? Ruth had reckoned six or seven weeks.

Sure enough, the following day, before I got round to checking with her, I had a sad phone call from Ruth; she was in floods.

"I'm not pregnant after all, is it too late to leave that out if you've mentioned it?"

I reassured her I hadn't, and she was desperately grateful, poor lass.

We got talking and found ourselves on the subject of Rory.

"He seemed to be very amused by something you'd left unsaid. I don't suppose you'd care to enlighten me."

"I'd have to know you rather better, Hazel," she said, intriguingly. "It's not the sort of thing that would make it into a family newspaper!"

"It doesn't concern Teddy, does it?" I said. "As a former boyfriend of yours, I mean."

All right, I'll admit that I was on a fishing trip.

"Only indirectly," said Ruth, doing absolutely nothing to satisfy my curiosity.

I got the story a few weeks later. Ruth and I were on separate girls' nights out in the Cellar Vie wine bar and she came across to say hello. We chatted about this and that and then, out of the blue, she said firmly but not truculently: "What you really want to know about is Teddy and me, don't you?"

"He doesn't still hanker after you, does he? I just worry about him all the time, since, well you know, since last year when he tried to kill himself."

"We all fret about him," she agreed. "But Teddy and I, it really was a brief fling. We were both first-year students and neither of us had any sexual experience at all. We just about managed to lose our virginity together, though it was all rather embarrassing and a bit of a mistake. However, we were still kind of semi-going out, or at least hanging around together, on the night of that party. Teddy had a bad cold and I decided to go anyway with a girlfriend. As soon as I saw Rory, I just knew that he was the one for me."

"Wow," I said. "Love at first sight, just you like you told me. And was it straight into the sack, as well? Sorry, too many questions, you don't have to answer that one."

"I might as well," she laughed. "After the party, Rory and I returned to his flat in the city centre. The other tenant must have been away for the weekend. We said our goodnights and went to separate bedrooms. I can't remember now why we didn't just leap on one another at the first opportunity. Maybe it was an intuitive thing; we'd both been drinking a lot, and wanted the first time to be something special, not an inebriated rough and tumble.

"The following morning, we were wearing old dressing gowns and sitting together on a battered sofa. Gradually, you know how it is, the space between us narrowed. I could see he was getting excited. I just grabbed him and asked him if it was all for me, or if he'd just woken up like that? He blushed and said it was a bit of both."

"There's nothing like a bit of honesty when it comes to sex," I said.

"That is more or less how I put it," laughed Ruth, almost spilling her gin and tonic as she grabbed my shoulder to keep her balance. "A *fortnight earlier I'd been a virgin, and there I was sounding like I'd slept with half the college rugby team."*

I was idly trying to work out how many men that would be. I couldn't tell you how many players there are on a rugby team. Jim once told me there were two kinds of rugby, so that might make a difference. But Ruth suddenly went all serious on me.

"You know, Rory and I really did appreciate your thoughtfulness. After such a long wait, I should have known it was too good to be true. Being back to square one is almost more than I can stand."

The National Diary

January 2009

My next move will be…

The column in which we try to help someone who is at a crossroads in his or her working life. This week we focus on:

Name: Edward Beresford
Age: 33

Employer: United and Valley Newspapers (*Cull Valley Evening Gazette*, daily paper in West Yorkshire)

Salary: £23,000 a year.

Marital status: Single

Higher education: honours degree in English, University of Devon; postgraduate journalism qualification, Cardiff.

Edward –
It's a pity that the public has such a low approval rating for your trade. In television dramas, hacks are usually as egregious and dissembling as those posh English characters that turn up in *Taggart* when there has been a white-collar murrdagh. And when the journalists in TV shows work for local newspapers, the writers can usually be relied on to add a soupçon of contempt.

You will no doubt have been taken aback from time to time by the patronising attitude of some professional people towards your trade, as if you were no more than a clerical worker: "*Cull Valley Evening Gazette*? We've all got to start somewhere, I suppose".

You are not alone. Who really has much of a clue about other people's trades? Librarians get less respect than bank officials, because people honour money more than they do books and learning; teachers are the subject of disparaging remarks from folk who were too thick, lazy or short of parental engagement to learn anything in their school days (although there is a growing, albeit grudging, respect for anyone willing to throw themselves into the maelstrom of secondary education).

This is all relevant to your situation, because it is easy to become depressed by such views, and even half believe them yourself. In your darker moments, you seem to see yourself as a failure, but this is not the case. You are not setting the world on fire but you are a solid all-round journalist who would be perfectly capable of performing well in a bigger arena. Don't forget that there are many writers on national 'quality' newspapers who cannot even knock out a well-honed first paragraph to a news story.

So don't be too downhearted or cynical about your current role. At the *Cull Valley Evening Gazette*, you are surrounded by some nice people, most of whom also do their job well or at least competently. It's true that there are some nasty individuals, but that's the case in any organisation. Wherever you work and whatever your line, there will always be three Hazel Moses or Stan Cartwrights for every 'Doc' Jekyll or 'Chuck' Thrower.

But, yes, we do take your point that you might need to move on at some point, not least because there appear to be no prospects for promotion and the money, never great, has got worse in recent years compared with the pay of other professional people. A generation ago, you were not that far from a par with teachers, for example. Remember, too, that you are in a contracting industry and that the days when you could have had a steady job on the local newspaper for life have long gone. As someone with no commitments, you could move to London and hustle for shift work on the national papers. You do say that you considered that course of action a few years ago but hesitated because of a brief romantic entanglement. It's not too late: if you've any contacts down there, now could be the time to make use of them.

What else? Well, your interest in buying and selling books might be something to build on, if you find an area in which you can specialise, such as modern first editions or old books on sport. You don't sound like the sort of person for whom public relations would have much appeal but there's good money in it. Alternatively, there could be some satisfaction in working as a press officer for a charitable organisation. You say that you have been ruminating recently on the need to give something back. How about VSO? Two years working in a Third World country would give you a very different perspective on life as well as providing memories and experiences that would last a lifetime.

Do try to give some serious thought to these ideas. It's as true as night following day that the more you put into life, the more you get out of it. Your decision to use your knowledge of books to help out at a charity shop sounds like a good start – just so long as you are sure that your reasons for doing so are genuinely altruistic, and not morally dubious.

On the Retro Road

Kenneth Thrower goes down Memory Lane to 'test drive' a 1966 Ford Anglia

My dad's first car was a Ford Anglia. He passed away recently and when I was clearing out his house, I came across an old warranty card which gives the engine number (100E 433495), key number (EP 646) and delivery date (2.9.57). You can imagine what a day of high excitement it was in the Thrower household when we all hit the road for our first Sunday outing, destination Greenwood Crags.

I also found an original brochure for the vehicle among Dad's effects. That took me back, all right. I remembered as if it were yesterday how delighted I'd been to learn that Miss Avis Scott, the well-known television and theatre actress, was a proud owner of the same car we had bought. Miss Scott was very enthusiastic about the colour and interior design of her deluxe model. She was pictured in Dad's brochure stepping out of her cream-coloured Anglia, near her London flat, wearing carefully chosen clothes, including crushed strawberry gloves, to complement the vehicle.

It was a great privilege recently to meet members of Cull Valley Anglia Owners' Club, and to 'test drive' a vehicle in the company of one of their most delightful members, Julia Yates. Julia's car is a later version than Dad's old Anglia. It's a bright-red (Julia calls it 'sunburst red') 1966 105E model in the style that most people are familiar with through the Harry Potter films, featuring the classic tightly-angled rear window, wide chrome grille and those prominent 'eye' headlamps.

"I'm really looking forward to putting her through her paces," I told Julia as we walked across the Horse and Groom car park to her immaculately-preserved vehicle.

"Him," Julia corrected me, as I settled myself in the driver's seat. "I call him Reggie. But he does have some feminine qualities, Kenneth," she agreed after some thought. "The smart upholstery, complementary colours and roominess were all designed with us ladies in mind, and I understand that Ford used to employ female styling experts to get the right look."

This Ford Anglia, it occurred to me, would have been making its debut, perhaps owned by a mini-skirted Kings Road chick, when England won the World Cup. I'm pleased to report that Reggie was as smooth as Bobby Charlton, elegant as Bobby Moore and tough as Nobby Stiles.

Julia reports that her architect husband, Anthony, bought Reggie 14 years ago, after he had been immaculately restored by a reluctant seller who was going abroad. When the couple were married, Julia took over responsibility for Reggie and, thanks to the help of a local enthusiast, he remains as pristine as ever. He performs well, too: there's good acceleration, combined with powerful pull at lower-engine speeds, and terrific road handling. You can really feel the road as Reggie takes the tightest corners with aplomb. Stepping back in motoring time, I rather enjoyed driving a car whose instruments panel doesn't resemble that of a fighter jet plane. The panel is both easy to see, and easy to read.

I remember Dad, who didn't pass his driving test until he was 30, complaining about how busy the roads were becoming in the mid-1960s. What would he make of modern driving conditions? Even in an old Ford Anglia, it's not easy to re-create the 1960s' motoring experience, when far fewer people were car owners and you often had the road to yourself.

Things change for the better as well as the worse, of course, and the specifications of modern cars knock their 60s' counterparts into a cocked hat: in-car entertainment, air conditioning, tinted windows, adjustable wing mirrors, central locking, you name it. We had none of these in our Anglia. Neither, of course, did we have air bags which must have saved a few lives in the decade or so since they became a feature of all new cars.

But these thoughts occurred later. As I negotiated the A8814 between Ainsley and Hexroyd, as carefully as the day I took my driving test, my efforts were all about returning Julia in comfort and safety to the Horse and Groom, meeting point for the Anglia enthusiasts who had given me such a warm welcome.

Julia loves her cars and prides herself, too, on the quality of her driving – she's an associate member of the Central Pennine Branch of the Institute of Advanced Motorists. She describes herself as "an exceptional driver". I'm sure she is and I take my hat off to her, for her lack of false modesty.

As we said farewell, it occurred to me that Julia and the other members of the Anglia Owners' Club had got the best of all motoring worlds.

At weekends, they can enjoy the fun of stepping back in time to a more innocent and uncomplicated era, then return to their high-spec modern automobiles (Julia's currently driving a top-of-the-range Golf) for the day-to-day business of commuting up and down the motorway to their workplaces in Manchester and Leeds.

Wherever you might be heading this weekend, happy motoring to you all!

Stories they cannot print

KENNETH THROWER.....

I was on the advertising team's side of the office floor the other day because our photocopying machine was on the blink. I was queuing behind the Moses girl, who was there for the same reason. I watched as she exchanged pleasantries, in that easy-going manner she has, with passing members of the sales force. A very neat little number, our Hazel. Perhaps not so little, as she is a trifle on the plump side. But she has untamed glossy black hair and an appealing smile. Minnie Driver, maybe, if I was casting her in a film. For one of her tribe she is not unattractive, and I've heard that her sister, Sally, a taller, more willowy version, is a real cracker.

I played with the idea of trying my luck last year with Hazel. I didn't get great vibes (very few smiles for me, and I'm not Asperger's so I can pick up the cues) and I decided not to risk it. As Hazel announced her wedding date the following week, it's fair to say that I saved myself from an embarrassing moment. And for the most part, I've behaved very well since then in general, managing to keep it zipped up. So much so that Mrs T's suspicious mind is clocking up more overtime than it does when I really am sniffing around. I'll tell her, say, that I'm going to meet a company's managing director regarding the Gazette Business of the Year competition. Yes, love, honestly. But does she believe me?

The Missus was similarly sceptical about my Sunday outing to meet the Cull Valley Anglia Owners' Club. When she saw my feature in the paper, Thrower Towers ran as close to hearing an apology as it is ever likely to get, though she couldn't resist adding: "You did seem quite taken with the Yates woman."

"She was quite bonny," I admitted. No point in denying it; I'd have been laughed out of Mrs T's kangaroo court.

Test driving a car with Julia sitting next to me wasn't easy. Her shapely legs and heady Miss Dior perfume didn't exactly aid concentration on the road but I did my best. In fact, I reckon that I did rather well. Julia was relaxed enough with my handling of Reggie to lie back in her seat and close her eyes. She even allowed her skirt to ride a little further up her thighs while she listened to Bad Company on the impressive CD player, her one concession in the Anglia to 21st century motoring.

Julia admits to being a 'rock chick' which accounts for the choice of band; an excellent selection, and the possibility that Feel Like Making Love might turn up brought on a little twinge. When that song duly appeared, after Silver, Blue and Gold if I remember correctly, and Julia started to sing along, there was nothing little about it.

"I suppose we should really be listening to swinging sixties' stuff, Wayne Fontana and the Mindbenders, and The Hollies," I said. "And The Kinks."

"Yes, and I suppose I ought to be wearing stockings, to get the period feel right," said Julia.

That's not the sort of observation a red-blooded male should be hearing on the approach to a notorious A8814 black spot. It was probably the most touch-and-go moment in Reggie's 40-plus years on the road. Pro that I am, I did however negotiate the bend safely enough. Then I found myself, forward by even Chuck Thrower's high standards, saying: "You should, Julia. Another time, perhaps."

"Is that an offer of lunch?" she said.

"Could be."

"By the way, what sign are you, Kenneth?"

"Pisces. It makes for a rather good combination with yours. Symbiotic, even."

When the ladies want to play that game, it's best to go along with them. It didn't occur to Julia that she hadn't actually told me what her sign was.

"Yes, Librans and Pisceans. It's a good combo," she agreed.

And when you're pushing 60 (though I could pass for early-50s, I'm slim, a non-smoker and I've got a full head of hair), you do begin to wonder when you might begin to lose the knack. Well, if I can score with the likes of Julia Yates, it just goes to show that there's still plenty of life in the old campaigner.

The National Diary

June 1992

Tears and tantrums as Teddy loses the plot

Our chief sports writer, Jon Stretford, reports from Hexroyd Tennis Club

How poignant now seem Kipling's words about meeting Triumph and Disaster, and treating those two impostors just the same.

Hexroyd Tennis Club witnessed one of the most remarkable comebacks in the history of its annual Under 18s' championship when, from match point down against Edward 'Teddy' Beresford, Tom Hogg recovered to win the match, the championship and, ultimately, the hand of Rachel Waterfall, the club's recent arrival who is as lovely and fragrant as her name.

The final score gives some indication of how the match turned round; Hogg triumphed by 5-7, 7-6, 6-1. What those bare facts cannot begin to conjure up was the fascinating contrast in styles, the tension throughout that remarkable second set and the horror on the faces of the Beresford camp as their man threw away the final set with a mixture of hopelessly optimistic shots, wild second serves and tantrums aimed at umpire Colin Sangster, a history teacher at Hexroyd Grammar School.

In the end it all hinged on a crucial call by Sangster. During the tie-break game, Hogg had looked like a man drinking in the last-chance saloon. At match point to Beresford, Hogg served powerfully but desperately into the net. Many spectators, including your correspondent, were convinced the second serve then went wide; victory for the admittedly below-par favourite, whose only defeat this summer had been in the quarter-finals of the senior tournament.

But no. Sangster deemed that the ball had clipped the line and, from that moment, Hogg had a new lease of life. He took the next two points to tie the match before Beresford's head had cleared, then abandoned his previously cautious approach, aggressively charging to the net at every opportunity to win six of the next seven games for a resoundingly conclusive triumph.

Some observers see fragility in Beresford's natural talent. It has been suggested that he lacks the killer instinct, letting lesser opponents back into the game rather than finishing them off. The usually equable 17-year-old atheist looked angrily to the skies, as if some malign force were finally punishing him for having lost his faith a few years earlier, and for the first time in his career he vented his fury on an official. The umpire had no choice but to issue an abuse warning. Finally, Sangster docked a point when Beresford suggested, quite ludicrously, that the match official favoured Hogg because he taught him at HGS.

There was a collective sharp intake of breath and many of the crowd, including the lovely Miss Waterfall, lost patience, transferring their allegiance to Hogg; from then on, there could only be one winner.

Which brings us back to Kipling, and his two impostors. Forgoing his usual modesty and reserve, Beresford had taken for granted his ultimate triumph. He could not handle success and neither could he take failure, ungraciously offering both Sangster and Hogg the most perfunctory of handshakes.

For the first time, the two camps in the crowd were entirely united as they saluted the new champion. Previously, they had been divided and partisan as the followers of Celtic and Rangers, Ajax and Feijenoord, River Plate and Boca Juniors. This had been the quintessential clash of styles, the compact, elegant and privileged Beresford, against the tall, lean, ferociously intelligent, tough-of-the-track Hogg, the council estate lad who will surely take the academic and sporting world by storm if, as teachers predict, he wins a place next year at Oxford or Cambridge.

Some spectators even booed Beresford, and Miss Waterfall thrust a sorrow-not-anger glance in his direction, like someone who'd had the scales removed from her alluring blue eyes.

Beresford lost more than a tennis match today.

CULL VALLEY EVENING GAZETTE

Monday 8 December 2008

It's Christmas...but is it art?

'Conceptualist' makes light work of upsetting the neighbours with his ironic 'Thank You, Lord'

By Jeannie Derby

A nationally-acclaimed artist who created an electric winter wonderland outside his house has been attacked by neighbours as "blasphemous" and "a vulgarian".

People have been flocking to Green Pastures, Hexroyd, from throughout the Cull Valley and beyond to see the phenomenal lights display, which its creator, 40-year-old Robbie Santiago, considers a work of art. It shows the Three Wise Men entering a department store and carries, in neon, the simple message: 'Thank You, Lord'.

The display has shocked locals, not least because the artist was welcomed with open arms when he took a six-month lease this summer, on the house in one of the Cull Valley's most select streets.

Architect and local resident Anthony Yates says: "Mr Santiago has been living in a beautiful house which he has, quite frankly, desecrated. The images are puerile and blasphemous, though I dare say that he thought he was conveying some sort of 'message' about consumerism. Perhaps he thinks that turns it into a work of art."

He said that he and his wife, Julia, had made Mr Santiago very welcome in Hexroyd and added: "In fact, everyone feels let down. I don't mind admitting that we enjoyed socialising with Robbie and meeting his sophisticated friends but he has now shown himself to be nothing more than a vulgarian, a Chav you might even say."

Mr Yates continued: "To be fair, he returned our hospitality and did invite us round to meet his many friends from the worlds of art, music and science. We listened to a string quartet one evening. What he's done now has shocked us to the core."

However, Mr Santiago, a recent convert to Conceptualist art, launched a robust defence of "Thank You."

He said: "These people have revealed a total ignorance about Conceptualism. This work of art isn't just about the images, you know, it's about the build-up to the installation, about reactions to

48

both me and the lights. I've worked bloody hard over the last six months to turn 'Thank You, Lord' into an important statement.

"Had I simply arrived from London in a shell suit and been seen on the doorstep drinking strong lager straight from the can, people would have said: "What did you expect?" when they saw the lights. Instead, what I have done is to gradually build a certain type of relationship with the local community by creating a particular persona.

"So what 'Thank You, Lord' has accomplished, with one fell swoop, is the destruction of their perception of me as a sophisticated incomer. It's a meaningful statement about the superficiality and hypocrisy of most human relationships.

"It might not be a comforting message, especially at this time of year, but it's a valid one. I hope that, if the Cull Valley remembers me for one thing, it will be as someone who encouraged them to reflect on more spiritual matters and to turn away from the pursuit of mammon and the worship of false prophets."

Residents of Green Pastures can console themselves with the knowledge that Mr Santiago's tenure on his current residence ends on December 31, and he has promised that the lights will come down before that, on Boxing Day. He is moving back to London in the New Year and is already being tipped for a 2009 Turner Prize nomination.

STORIES....JEANNIE DERBY....

Julia Yates has, I am fully aware, something of a reputation but I knew nothing about her fling with Robbie Santiago. It was strange finding out about the affair from her husband.

That Christmas lights piece was off-the-diary, as we reporters call a story that we've picked up under our own steam or via a good contact. Anthony Yates had rung me first thing to grumble about Santiago's lights. I agreed with his observations and suggested that I should interview him.

"I've got a couple of good pictures on my camera," said Anthony.

"Can you bring it in? We might even make today's paper, always assuming I can also get hold of Santiago for his side of things and have it written up by midday. The news editor's tearing his hair out, because a big story's just gone belly-up."

When Anthony arrived 20 minutes later he was positively bristling with indignation.

"Can I get you a coffee, or maybe a soothing cup of herbal tea would be better?"

"This isn't funny, Jeannie. What I told you on the phone is only the half of it."

"So what's the reaction of other neighbours been?"

"They're all pretty shocked, especially as everyone in the neighbourhood has made him so welcome. We all feel let down. I don't mind admitting that we enjoyed socialising with Santiago and meeting his sophisticated friends but he has now shown himself to be nothing more than a vulgarian, a Chav you might even say."

"He initiated some social gatherings, before the lights business?"

"Well, yes, Jeannie, to be fair he did return some of our hospitality and invited us round to meet his many friends from the worlds of art, music and science. We listened to a string quartet one evening. What he's done now has shocked us to the core."

"And what did Julia make of him?"

"Julia," he said, "was exceedingly welcoming to Robbie Santiago. They spent a lot of time in each other's company, especially when I was out of town because of my work. Santiago's mother died quite recently and, as your tabloid brethren would say, Julia comforted him."

He'd started that sentence quietly enough, and gradually worked himself up into a real lather.

"I'm rather assuming that is off the record, Anthony?"

"Feel free to drop the gentlest of hints in your copy. I'm sure you're experienced enough to know what you can get away with."

The National Diary

January 2009

Say goodbye with flowers

Michaelmas daisies were my girlfriend's parting gift

As Britain's students prepare to return for the second term of the academic year, Teddy Beresford recalls a poignant moment from his university days

I've often been accused of putting Rachel Waterfall on a pedestal. I was, after all, 16 years old when we met. For an impressionable teenage boy who's never even had a girlfriend that's a highly vulnerable age. I truly believe that I've never since come across anyone so appealing, although Ruth Fitzpatrick at Devon University came quite close.

I can recall our first meeting as though it were yesterday. A group of us were sitting in Dr Bob Finnigan's room, waiting for our first seminar on the history of literary criticism. I'd already heard a lot about Dr Finnigan, the department's resident Marxist and Structuralist, who with his long, grey hair and Zapata moustache looked like a throwback to the previous generation of university teachers. Finnigan had only recently relaxed his antagonistic stance to the bourgeois concept of individual creativity sufficiently to allow for the concept of the author; I'd like to have been there when a fresher said to him: "You mean that Sue Townsend didn't really write Adrian Mole." But he also had a fearsome reputation as a stickler for good use and understanding of English grammar. He'd put students on the spot by asking them to define a clause or to explain the hanging participle.

Finnigan had left a note on the door telling us to enter, and we were all awaiting his arrival with some trepidation when Ruth bounced in, slightly breathless.

"Phew, traffic," she said, economically. "Where is he then?"

While less of an English rose than Rachel, Ruth had a delightfully open and friendly face, and neat, gamine features, complemented by short, wavy, Roman-style close-cropped hair. No one in our timid little group had quite dared to break the ice, but Ruth quickly got everyone talking as she examined the pictures on Finnigan's wall.

"That's child abuse. For all she knows she could be celebrating a BOGOF at Tesco," she said, examining an image of a tiny girl wrapped around a huge Cuban flag, giving a V for Victory salute. Other pictures dedicated to the ongoing struggle to create an eternal dictatorship of the proletariat included a poster in bright red, with something written in Russian below an image of Karl Marx.

"Workers of the world unite," said Finnigan cheerfully as he walked in, raising his fist in a Pavlovian response to our examination of his hero.

"I think Finnigan's bark is much worse than his bite," said Ruth later, as we sat together over a coffee in the union bar. "He seems quite nice, politics and daft literary theories aside."

"You're probably right," I said, "But I'm glad he wasn't there when that girl said she thought the poster of Marx was Lenin. You'd think she'd have had the guile to know that she should have known who he was, even if she didn't, if you follow me."

"Just about," she smiled, encouragingly. I seemed to be making a good impression, and I cast around for a follow-up.

"Didn't know John Cooper Clarke was still going strong," I said, looking at a poster on the wall. "He's here on Friday."

"I saw him in Leeds a few years ago," she said. I suppose it was a sign we were getting on well that I hadn't fallen back on the usual, early question about where you come from. Her accent was neutral, verging on posh, not Yorkshire.

"I wouldn't mind seeing him again," she continued.

I've missed a few open goals in my time but even I could hardly have blown that one.

"We could go, if you like," I said, tapping the ball home effortlessly from the edge of the six-yard box.

And that's how our brief courtship started. I very enthusiastic (verging on the puppyish if I'm honest), she less obviously committed. She went home to Leeds one weekend, quite a schlep, and I was disappointed that she didn't suggest we go together. I thought that might have marked the end of the affair, such as it was, but the night after she returned we both drunk a bit too much and went to bed for the one and only time. It wasn't a bells-ringing and lights-flashing moment; the combination of inexperience and alcohol ruled that one out. But I'm sure that, given the opportunity, we'd have made a better go of it.

I never got the chance because I went down with a bad cold two days later. On the next Saturday, there was a party in a nearby hall of residence. I cried off because I still felt below par. That afternoon Ruth came round to see how I was, and brought me a beautiful bunch of Michaelmas daisies.

"Hope you don't mind, I think I'll go anyway, a couple of my friends have got their eye on a chemist called Rory. Drop-dead gorgeous, I'm told. Be fun to see how it pans out."

But it was Ruth who took Rory's fancy, and the feeling was entirely reciprocated. Ruth, trying not to look as happy as she felt, did the decent thing and broke it to me as gently as she could. She came round to see me again a few days later. She was pleased to see that the Michaelmas daisies were still there; I hadn't thrown them out in a hissy fit. Nevertheless, I wasn't sorry to say goodbye to the flowers when they finally began to wilt.

My dislike of Rory lasted for about a minute. He turned out to be one of the nicest guys I'd ever met, and the way he and Ruth looked at one another told me that there could be no way back.

There are some things that you just have to accept with good grace.

Julia's Journal

Anthony's a sweetie. This morning, as ever, he brings me breakfast. I've made it nice and easy for him. I set up the tray before I came to bed — teacup and saucer, small teapot with two bags, knife, plate with butter and Frank Cooper's at the edge, egg cup on a saucer with salt, white pepper and a spoon.

He kisses me on the cheek and says: "I'll be late tonight, church wardens' meeting. Don't let the toast get cold."

After he's gone, the first thing I do is to check my stars in the Cull Valley Evening Gazette, and that just sweeps away any little worries about my next move. There's a rare alignment of Venus and Mercury. I don't ever recall such an astrological event, which is good news for Arians, like Teddy. And as for Librans, like me, how about this? 'A vibrant and passionate new arrival on the scene'. Well, that's just got to be Teddy, it all fits. He really is rather lovely. Poor old Kenny 'Chuck' Thrower. We'll have to let him down ever so gently.

Now, what to wear today? I spend some time in my dressing room, opening and closing wardrobe doors and drawers and looking at all my shoes. Then I have a quick peek out of the window. The weather dictates the shoes and the shoes dictate the outfit, I always say. My little mantra.

Teddy clocked me at the charity shop, no question, and the feeling was entirely mutual. He could be just what I'm looking for, something beyond a quick fling. Barbara Machin put a damper on things, as is her wont, when she told me that he was a journalist on the Cull Valley Evening Gazette; hardly the sexiest or best paid of jobs. But it turns out his parents are doctors who live in one of those fancy Swiss-style houses in Geneva Row. His mother could even be the same woman I once wrote to in her capacity as the Gazette's agony aunt. I don't suppose she'd remember.

I wonder if Teddy got into such a tizz, when he read in the Gazette that I'd called him "our hero", that he had to go to the office toilet to pleasure himself, in anticipation of the delights to come? And I wonder if he thought to himself: "Julia Yates, where have I heard that name before?" – then looked me up on the electronic files thingy, or whatever they've got at the Gazette. I'd love to have been a fly on the wall when he discovered that I was the same Julia Yates, an associate member of the Central Pennine Branch of the Institute of Advanced Motorists, who'd gone out for a drive with sad, horny old Kenneth Thrower; and, more to the point, the same Julia Yates who made Robbie Santiago so welcome. Yes, we all know what that was code for. Anthony couldn't resist that little dig.

Tomorrow's the day that really matters. That's when I'll really turn the screw and make my big impression on Teddy. He's coming in to help out for the first time; I'm told that he often has a mid-week day off work from the newspaper because of his Saturday shift.

Why am I sure he's so struck on me? Well, most men are! And here's a question for you: is it a coincidence that Teddy has chosen a Tuesday, the same day of the week that he made his rare book find, and therefore more likely to be one of the days when I am helping out? On balance, probably not!

Beresford's Beat

This week we welcome our new columnist, Teddy Beresford, who kicks off by revealing his hidden depths

In his youth, the artist Matisse was one of a group of men who agreed to be hypnotised.

His friends were persuaded that they were in a verdant forest, filled with flowers. Matisse wanted to surrender to the spell and join them, but persisted in saying that it wasn't working. On the floor, there was nothing but carpet. In later life, when faced with any kind of worldly temptation, Matisse would say: "I can still see the carpet."

Reading this story recently reminded me that, in the mid 1990s, I was among a small band of people who became hooked on a form of self-induced mesmerisation called autostereograms. 'Small band' is, I would guess, about right. Autostereograms weren't a craze of yo-yo or football sticker proportions; those of us who had the patience to master them were in a minority.

For the benefit of readers still scratching their heads, autostereograms were complex and apparently abstract pictures containing a hidden 3D image. Making the shape appear before your eyes was the tricky bit and there were several techniques. For me, the best way was simply to let my eyes go slightly blurred at a distance of a foot from the page and concentrate hard. The image would usually leap out at me within ten seconds.

I had an advantage. When I was a small boy, I had a trick of looking at myself in a mirror without blinking. I kind of stared through myself and I could turn my face into that of a three-eyed monster. So when these autostereogram books appeared, all I had to do was use my old mirror-staring technique.

The other day, I was rooting around at home and came across a *Hidden Depths* Autostereogram Notebook, published in 1994, when I was 19. I'd used it as a basic diary, but must have spent a lot of time examining the pictures.

"No call from Gill, [my girlfriend at the time, who was on the verge of dumping me]. Buried fish image took seven seconds to appear," I'd written; "Looks like it's going to be another Mud-style Christmas, ie Lonely. Butterfly picture 12 seconds."

Once I'd picked up the image, like looking into a large hologram, I could hold it, with a minimum of concentration, indefinitely. This part of the exercise was restful, and had a similar effect on me, I imagine, to what yoga and meditation is aiming to achieve. In other respects, I've always considered myself to be as sceptical as Matisse about anything which carries a whiff of mesmerisation, or the threat of being out of control. There's nothing wrong with that, though there are dangers in being excessively cautious and analytical.

Life delivers all manner of temptations and opportunities to our door. When we are tempted by some irresistible but potentially risky proposition, analysis is vital. Lose sight of the carpet and you could be saying goodbye to the safe path that prevents you from straying into a forest full of trap doors.

But opportunities are a different kettle of fish. Disraeli said that the secret of success in life was to recognise that your moment had arrived at last and, in current parlance, to go for it. It's often said that we regret the things we failed to do rather than the mistakes we actually made. At the same time, we speculate on why such and such a person has risen in the world while someone more talented has done very little. Perspiration counts for a lot but so does the ability to know when to act and when to walk away or do nothing.

That, I think, is what ultimately divides life's successful people from the low or non-achievers.

I wonder what I'll be doing in ten years time, and whether I will feel fulfilled? For me, as for everyone, it will probably depend on the ability to distinguish temptation from opportunity.

Sometimes you need to see the carpet, sometimes you don't.

STORIES...TEDDY BERESFORD.....

I was lucky to join the Gazette when Bill Blanchflower was the editor. Bill was a large and genial man who, on the hottest days in summer, would dip into his own pocket and deposit a pile of ice creams and lollies on the news desk.

"It's a tonic for the troops," he said on one occasion.

"And exciting for the veterans," I added, as our senior resident in editorial, Reuben Parfitt, helped himself to a Kinky.

Bill loved rock music. At my interview, his opening question was: "What's the first record you ever bought?" I looked at the pictures of Jimi Hendrix and Leonard Cohen on the wall, and debated whether to re-write history with a precocious and sophisticated choice.

"The Power of Love, Jennifer Rush," I said, settling for the truth.

"Hmm. First album?"

"I think I was 13 or 14 before I got into buying albums. It must have been Don't Be Afraid of the Dark, Robert Cray Band. On vinyl."

"Better," he allowed.

It wasn't the most taxing cross-examination; I think Stan Cartwright had put in a good word and Bill just wanted to make sure I looked okay. Bill was the human face of newspaper editors, someone who preferred the men to the officers, which made for an uneasy relationship with the company's directors. Two years after I arrived he jumped ship, before he could be pushed, for a lecturing post at a former polytechnic in London.

The new editor was a man called Mark McClair and things would never be the same again; certainly not for Stan, whose career went into free-fall. Curiously, though, it was McClair who offered me the opportunity to write Beresford's Beat.

*"They tell me that you've got a rather **left**-field way of looking at life," he said, putting the stress in the wrong place. Maybe you would like to write a weekly column offering us your view of the world."*

I wasn't naïve enough to be flattered; a freelance columnist had taken her bat home for some reason. I was a ready-made, no-cost replacement who would do it on top of my other duties. Still, there's a little vanity in all of us; I liked the idea of seeing my face at the top of the page once a week. In those days, I must have thought that it would be good for my cuttings file, too.

"Not a bad start," said the editor, collaring me by the drinks machine after my piece about Matisse and autostereograms appeared. That was as close to a compliment as you could expect from McClair.

"Thanks, Boss," I said.

"But be careful you don't get too abstract, we're in the Cull Valley, not Paris."

"Fair enough, I'll remember that."

"Oh, and by the way," McClair said, turning back like Columbo, after I thought I'd been dismissed: "I suppose in a column like yours you'll be employing a light touch. Try to keep religion and politics out of it? We don't want to offend the readers, do we?"

"No, of course not," I said.

I've never concerned myself much with politics. Religion, however, is an itch that I just have to scratch now and then.

The Badger Hill School Telegraph

October 1985

A lesson in football skills from an expert

By Edward Beresford

Boys and girls in Ainsley had an exciting afternoon during the summer holidays when they got a free lesson in football skills.

Barry Donachie, Ainsley Athletic's skilful midfield player, gave his "master class" in Geneva Row, Ainsley.

Six children, including four pupils at Badger Hill Primary School, were coached in the right way to kick, control and pass the ball by one of Athletics' first-team regulars.

The event was arranged on the spur of the moment by Barry, who had spotted the boys and girls having a kick around in a garden.

Barry, who is a window cleaner when he is not playing football, said: "I was taking my lunch break during my round and saw the kids having a three-a-side match. When I finished my ham and tomato sandwiches, I asked if I could join in.

"One of the girls said 'why don't you give us a lesson in how to play, Barry' and I thought 'well, why not'."

He added: "I was very impressed by the standard of play, and everyone was very keen to listen and learn. I hope that they are all equally 'on the ball' with their school work!"

STORIES....TEDDY.....

"We've a new pupil joining us today, boys and girls," said our form teacher, Miss Finney. "Perhaps you'd like to introduce yourself, Tom."

The new boy, a gangly lad who was a head taller than most of us, stood up.

"My full name's Tom Robert Hogg and I'm ten years old. Me and my mum, that is my mum and I," he corrected himself, "my mum and I have recently moved to the Meadow Croft estate from Ashgrove Vale. I am already friends with Edward Beresford because we are in the same Cub pack, and I support Hexroyd Park Avenue."

There were a few titters over Tom's choice of football team, and considerably more over his surname. The form bully, Wayne Dixon, said "oink, oink" loudly enough for a few nearby kids to hear. Tom, who could look after himself, picked up on this; Dixon might live to regret it, I thought.

During the first break, Dixon decided that Tom had to be officially "welcomed".

"Smelly 'Ogg," he shouted across the playground, "are you a yeller belly or can yer fight?"

"Don't ever call me that, or you'll rue the day," said Tom.

"What's rue the day when it's at home?" said Dixon.

"Get a fucking dictionary and find out."

The growing audience gasped as if the film's villain, not dead after all, had risen for one last lunge. The 'F' word was not then in common usage among Cull Valley children of pre-secondary school age. Tom sauntered across to Dixon, looking almost friendly, then punched him so hard in the stomach that I winced. Next thing, he was sitting on top of Dixon, long legs and arms submerging his would-be tormentor. A crowd, suddenly transformed into an excited mob of Dickensian urchins, surrounded them; some, encouraged by me as the chief cheerleader, were rooting for Tom.

"What's my name?" said Tom, punching the ground threateningly close to Dixon's face.

"Hogg," said Dixon, less convincingly now, nervously including the aitch as he did when corrected by Miss Finney.

Tom raised his arm again above Dixon, rotating his wrist as if he had a lasso.

"Christian name, please."

"It's Tom...Tom," said Dixon.

"Are you sure?"

"Yes."

"Positive?"

"Positive."

"Pozi-wozz?"

"Pozi-wozz."

"Pozzi-wozz fozz?"

"Pozzi-wozz fozz."

The teacher on playground duty came round the corner, blowing a whistle.

"It's not very nice sitting on Wayne just because you're bigger than he is," she said to Tom, too late to prevent Dixon's humiliation.

"Sorry," said Tom.

"Sorry, what?"

"Sorry, Mrs I-don't-know-your-name-yet."

I giggled.

"It's typical of you to laugh at something silly like that, Edward Beresford. Play nicely from now on. I'll be watching you very closely, Tom Hogg."

That afternoon, Miss Finney outlined one or two projects for the forthcoming weeks.

"This term we're going to produce our own newspaper. I expect that most of you will have seen the Cull Valley Evening Gazette in your mum and dad's houses, and maybe a national paper too, such as the Times or the Daily Mail. Can anyone give me a difference between the Cull Valley Evening Gazette and a national paper?"

"The national paper has pictures of ladies with no clothes on," my friend Paul Hopkinson, the form comedian, suggested.

Miss Finney, who was game for a laugh, gave Paul her watch-yourself-laddie stare while doing her best not to look amused.

Tom Hogg said: "The Cull Valley Evening Gazette gives you local news, things that have happened where we live. The national newspapers give you stories from right round the country, and from other parts of the world as well when something very important has happened like the World Cup or a war."

"Very good indeed. So what kind are we going to produce?"

"A national paper," said Paul.

"You'll be producing a newspaper full of eleven and twelve times tables if you don't watch your step, Paul Hopkinson. Another question – does anyone know what an editor does on a newspaper?"

No one spoke; I could see Tom itching to answer but not wanting to look like too much of a clever clogs.

"Have you got any ideas, Tom?" said Miss Finney, spotting his enthusiastic bottom shuffle.

"The editor's the boss, Miss. He..."

"Or she..."

"Or she, Miss, decides on the contents of the paper."

"Yes, the contents of the paper" said Miss Finney. "What do we mean by that?"

"What goes in the paper, Miss. The stories and the pictures that go with them, and all the football on the back pages," I offered.

"Very good. So, in our paper, everyone will write an article."

"Suppose nothing has happened to us that's worth writing down, Miss?" said Paul.

"Everyone has got a story to tell. It could be whatever is most important in your life at the moment such as a new baby brother or sister, getting a family pet, or even an exciting place you went on holiday this summer and what you did there. I'm after true stories – or reports, as they are called – things that really did take place. So, I don't want made-up nonsense about Hexroyd Park Avenue beating Manchester United at Wembley in the FA Cup Final. I'll be coming round the class to help you to decide what to write about, and we are also going to need an editor. That person will help us to decide which reports go on which pages in our little newspaper. Our editor will also write an introduction on the front page, telling our readers – our friends and our mums and dads – about the paper and what they can expect to find in it. We will also have to find a name for our paper."

The editorship was put to a class vote; a couple of old regime die-hards stuck with Wayne Dixon but the triumphant Tom Hogg was overall winner.

"I think I ought to have a deputy, Miss," said Tom.

"Who do you think would be a suitable choice?" she asked.

"Edward Beresford," he said.

"Good, as long as he stops looking out of the window at the girls playing netball, and puts his mind to the job," said Miss Finney.

Our teacher's cousin was the managing director of The Finney Press, a local printing firm. He agreed to produce a small edition of Badger Hill School Telegraph, a four-page broadsheet. We made two visits, once to see our stories on bromide paper, being pasted together by a compositor, to create each page, and again to see the newspaper coming off the presses. It was exciting stuff, seeing in print my article about the impromptu football coaching session my friends and I had received from Barry Donachie.

"This is Tom Hogg, our editor," said Miss Finney, when we were introduced to her cousin at the printer's.

"Ah, that really is nice to see, very pleased for you, Tom," said Bob Finney, mysteriously. Grown-up methods of communication fascinated me; what a strange way of putting things.

Wayne Dixon produced our biggest article (the lead story, Miss Finney called it) about how his uncle from Los Angeles had made him a guitar. Wayne, coming from what in mid-1980s Cull Valley was still called a broken home, had many uncles. Paul Hopkinson wrote about a visit to his mother's family in Naples. Paul's dad sponsored the paper and we published an advertisement for his butcher's business. The best story came from a boy whose sister was the Cull Valley Carnival Queen. She'd been lifted by helicopter out of the Grand Canyon with a broken ankle ("So, you see, she really did want to travel," said Miss Finney, a joke that went over our heads). As this had already featured in the Evening Gazette, Miss Finney said it shouldn't be our lead story. We needed an "exclusive", one that had not previously appeared elsewhere, she explained. So Wayne got the vote and regained a shred of street-cred.

Barry Donachie had said to me: "You've certainly got a great right foot but concentrate on your school work unless you want to end up doing my job."

I didn't include that in my article for Miss Finney because I didn't want to sound big-headed, and also I thought that being a window cleaner was a perfectly reasonable thing to do.

I was sorry that I hadn't been able to write about the 1985 FA Cup Final, in which Hexroyd Park Avenue playmaker Edward Beresford lashed an unstoppable volley past the despairing arms of Manchester United goalkeeper Gary Bailey, to bring the historic trophy back to Yorkshire for the first time since 1972.

But, I thought, I can do all that on my own if I create a newspaper at home, to record the big events, both real and imaginary, in my life.

Wednesday 6 February 2008

First love never dies

As St Valentine's Day looms, Jeannie Derby goes into Hexroyd and Ainsley to pop this simple question to a few shoppers: 'Do you remember your first love?'

- Hughie McGiven of Ainsley (pictured right) was smitten with a girl in his Sunday School class when he was seven-years-old. He always longed to sit next to her for the Bible story. "She was called Kelly and she had three straps on her sandals, which I thought was very stylish. I never did quite have the nerve to talk to her, and the following summer her family moved down south. Who knows, she might have turned out to be the love of my life!"

- Harvey Lazarus of Hexroyd (above) fell for Gilly, the girl next door. Her younger sister was a friend of his little brother, Ephraim. "I used to go round to tell Fima, as we called Ephraim, that supper was ready, even if it wasn't, as an excuse to catch a glimpse of Gilly. Fima realised what I was up to and told me that I didn't stand a chance because she already had a boyfriend. We were always very supportive of one another!

- Rachel Waterfall (left) lives in London. She was visiting the Cull Valley where her parents still live. "I met Teddy at the local youth club when I was 16 and my family had just moved here from Devon. He was lovely but it was unrequited – he clearly liked me but 'not like that' as we used to say. So my real first love was my husband, Tom. We've been together now for 16 years!"

STORIES... JEANNIE DERBY...

"Teddy? That's Teddy Beresford, isn't it?" I said to Rachel Waterfall. "I work with him at the Gazette."

"Really? I'm sure that Tom will be interested to hear that. They were in the Cubs together," she said.

I did a few more of those 'vox-pop' interviews. Rachel agreed to be photographed and her picture was the one used most prominently; she was very easy on the eye, as our snapper put it. He did full justice to her.

That night Hazel and I went together to the leaving-do of a young reporter called Tony. Teddy didn't show and Hazel, in the light of my 'vox-pop', started to worry about him.

"He never misses a farewell bash, and he's a friend of Tony's. I think I should go round to his house and see that he's okay. Can you drive me?"

As the office teetotaller, I was also the office cabbie. I started to object but Hazel cut me short.

"No, we're going now," she said.

"Well, we can go and hold his hand, or you can hold his hand and I'll make the tea, when I've finished my J2O."

"No, Jeannie, you will pick up your fucking car keys NOW."

I did as I was told; no one spoke like that to the office God botherer without good reason.

"Teddy did the collection, bought the farewell present and supplied the choicest anecdotes about Tony for Thrower's speech," Hazel said as I drove in to Ainsley. "There's no way he'd want to miss this gig. Some solicitor stood him up the other week and he's been banging on about how she was out of his league. And now he's discovered that his love supreme, the sainted Rachel fucking Waterfall, might have carried a torch for him after all. God knows what sort of a state he's in."

At Geneva Row, the lights were on but no one answered, although Teddy's car was in the driveway. I began to feel sick, as well as angry with myself for my lack of concern.

"Are we going to break in, or ask the neighbours for help?" I said.

"No need, there's a spare key under a stone in the rockery."

Teddy was completely out of it, his face was a strange colour and his breathing pattern most peculiar. A tube of paracetamol lay on the

68

coffee table and the room stank of whisky; whatever Teddy hadn't drunk had been absorbed by the carpet. While waiting for the ambulance we marched him round and round the living room and managed to make him sick a few times. He was semi-conscious and kept muttering: "Sorry, Hank, sorry," whatever that might have meant.

Teddy must have worked his way through a lot of pills and scotch, but the medics got to grips with the stomach pump in time enough to prevent any liver damage. He was groggy for a few days. However, thanks to Hazel's timely intervention, he was never in any danger.

TEDDY

I could have written myself into a 𝔑ational 𝔇iary article about the aftermath of a suicide attempt. But, for once, sod the 𝔑ational 𝔇iary. Some things are just too big.

People say the strangest things in hospital, especially following an operation. I felt pretty awful and sore as hell after the stomach pump. At some point later I woke up from a deep sleep to see my parents sitting there.

"*Are You Sure Hank Done It This Way*," I said.

Mum and Dad looked truly crumpled.

"Hank?" they said as one.

"It's a song by Waylon Jennings, one of Henry's favourites. I've just been dreaming about Hank, he's written a novel. When is he coming to see me?"

"Oh Teddy," Mum said gently, then hesitated over what should come next.

I saved her the trouble by bursting into tears. I was overcome by exhaustion and emotion. Two ideas raced round my head, vying for pole position: horror over what I'd done to myself and misery as I remembered that my friend Hank would never be coming to see me.

A psychologist came on to the ward to look me over. My contrition, I am pretty certain, was absolutely, 100 per cent clear.

We talked for a while and he said: "You're clearly a young man with some issues that need addressing, not least depression. The best thing we can do is get you to see a cognitive behavioural therapist."

So once a week, for about two months, I went down to the local health centre where Melanie Gold, my therapist, persuaded me to open up about myself. I had been sceptical about the whole business, but Melanie's soft and faintly husky voice, when she rang to confirm our appointment, helped me to make my mind up. Perhaps fortunately, she turned out to be a matronly, distraction-free figure, and there's no doubt that at least some of what she said was helpful. I filled out workbooks, designed to challenge what Melanie called "unhelpful thinking". The most significant negative thought was a tendency to blame myself for missing the opportunities life threw my way, while giving myself credit for absolutely nothing that had happened in my past.

Melanie also had me writing a weekly diary about my frame of mind.

"Still getting sudden attacks of negative thoughts," I wrote one week. *"They can emerge out of nowhere. Would you believe one started when I was walking past the local branch of Dixon's and a tennis match was on TV. A player disputed an umpire's decision and that was enough to set me off. It's a poison seeping through my brain, giving the most innocuous incidents a toxic edge. I do know that these thoughts will go away eventually but they can be exhausting. When they do, it's like the after-effects of one of my migraines, which always leave me knackered.*

"The biggest single issue is a tendency to pick on an incident from my past and replay it endlessly. Sometimes I select it myself. On other occasions, as with the tennis umpire in Dixon's, it's chosen for me.

"Worst of all is when I wake up like this in the morning. I sometimes lie in bed running through some mad moments from my past, like a juke box programmed to decide randomly which record should be played next...."

I think Melanie's greatest achievement, if that isn't putting it too grandly, was to see the pattern in my behaviour, the endless rewinding to specific incidents which too often led back to Rachel Waterfall.

It's not easy to see me ever being entirely out of the woods – I suspect that the *National Diary* will remain irresistible – and Melanie said during one session: "At least choose your topics carefully for your diary," as if we were agreeing on some compromise deal for my future introspective excesses.

On another day she said something that struck a chord. "Try flipping a coin. Think about decisions you made that turned out for the best. For example, if you hadn't complained about being put in the *Gazette*'s Birthday Club at the age of 21, or

71

been willing to spend a week working for no pay, you might never have ended up on the staff."

"You'll have to sell it better than that, my job at the bloody *Gazette*," I said, "Though I take your point." I had to admit that she was a fine listener, good at recalling the details of stories I'd told her.

"Teddy, you've said yourself the job's perfectly tolerable bar the money, and you could have ended up in far worse places, or as an aimless arts graduate in McDonald's or Waterstone's. And you'd never have met lovely people like Stan, Hazel and Jeannie."

"Or Frances Jekyll, Kenneth Thrower and Mark McClair for that matter," I argued.

"Well, isn't that another part of the problem? You're doing it again. You need to accentuate the good side in the decisions you've made. Even our less-than-perfect life choices can have positive outcomes. Focus on them."

And, funnily enough, it seems to be working, for the most part. For a while after the incident with the pills and the scotch, Mum and Dad tip-toed round me, scared to say the wrong thing. Or I'd catch them examining me intently, for some indication that I was about to dash out and throw myself in front of a juggernaut. That was never going to happen, as the psychologist in the hospital worked out straightaway. And using my coin-flipping technique, I'm generally coping by and large much better.

A few months down the line, Dad said: "You don't even like whisky, why couldn't you have gone for a bottle of the blended rather than my best Talisker?"

For a couple of seconds Mum looked mortified, as if Dad had said something in shocking taste. Then the three of us laughed.

At that moment, I knew that they knew that we were all going to be fine.

CULL VALLEY EVENING GAZETTE

Friday January 9 2009

A day in their life

HAZEL MOSES spends a day with charity shop volunteers

They're a cheerful crowd at Ainsley Battling Cancer (ABC). Manager Cath Wilson greets me with a sunny smile and the rest of the team look up from their duties to say a friendly hello to the new girl. I'm here to spend a day trying to sort out the wheat from the chaff among the mountain of goods coming into the shop (ABC is very well supported), to help on the till, and generally to find out what a working day is like for the volunteers who man these shops which are an increasingly prominent feature of our high streets.

Cath's a middle-aged mum who admits that she came here initially because she was at a loose end, in the days when the charity was called Ainsley Against Cancer.

She says: "I'd been a full-time housewife after starting a family. With the kids at college, I'd suddenly got rather a lot of time on my hands. After I'd completed an Open University course, one day a week in the shop became two, then three….I love working here, you see human nature at its best. People are very generous with their donations – and with their purchases, too. It's amazing how often you will hear someone saying: 'Don't bother with the change, Love,' as they hand you a fiver or a ten-pound-note for something that costs rather less."

There are a few Caths working in the town's two ABC shops. But there are some eager young helpers, too. In the case of Andy Dougan, a profoundly deaf economics graduate, the work has led to a paid job elsewhere.

Cath says: "One local businessman was so impressed by Andy's manner and people skills that he's now been offered a 'proper' job. It's an indictment of the attitude of many employers that he had been unable previously to find paid work which matched his talents."

It's lovely at ABC to see all age groups mingling together and getting on so well. Andy tells me that he has become a good friend of Ray Hutton, a retired woodwork teacher who comes in

73

occasionally and who makes fabulous dolls' houses which he sells to raise money for ABC.

Then there's Julia Yates, a young housewife who's here twice a week, and who has arrived a few minutes late because of traffic and parking problems.

"Sorry! I'm ready to get cracking now," she says, revealing the enthusiasm for the job that typifies the team at Ainsley Battling Cancer.

As it happens, I'm not the only person lending a hand for the first time at ABC. The other newcomer is Teddy Beresford, my colleague and friend at the *Gazette*.

Teddy's involvement with ABC is a story in itself, as some of our readers will recall. A few weeks ago he discovered a rare first edition on the shelves here. He offered his services looking through new book stock and from now on will now be coming into the shop on the first Tuesday of each month.

It is an unusually quiet day but there are plenty of ways to make myself useful. I do some tidying up and come up with a few thoughts for a window display with a Swinging Sixties' theme. I also become the Ainsley Battling Cancer shop's gofer girl, making brews – they like their cuppas at ABC! – and to-ing and fro-ing between the shop and the upstairs stock room where Julia is helping Teddy with the books. More than 200 had arrived during the last month and they need to be unpacked from musty boxes and damp carrier bags. On this occasion, Teddy finds just one that interests him personally, an original green Penguin *Maigret*.

"I collect these myself," he says, offering Cath a sum which strikes me as very generous, and far more than the shop could charge.

Following a few discussions with Cath about how much customers are likely to pay for these books (most, he thinks, will get no more than 50 pence to £1) Teddy comes up with higher and lower prices – ballpark figures which can be adjusted up or down a little depending on how sales are going, he says.

We have a flurry of visitors to the shop during the last hour of opening, perhaps as a result of a sudden downpour. Quite a few people have never been in the shop before and are impressed by the range and quality of some of the goods on display. ABC sells delightful hand-made greetings cards and tasty looking fair-trade chocolate, as well as second-hand goods.

There are some generous donations, too, during the day. At one point, someone brings in a really good selection of folk and roots CDs, not the sort of music you usually associate with charity shops which tend to be heavy on Mantovani, show songs and the more dated sounds from the 1980s.

"Oh, Jeffrey Woodworth," says Barbara Machin, another ABC regular, looking at the top CD with its sticker 'Mercury Prize Nominee, 2003'. "The man who sang *Tory Lady in Red*. We'll get a few bob for him."

At the end of the day, Cath pronounces herself delighted with the day's takings, especially after such a slow morning. ABC can always make use of a few more hands on deck. If you would like to help out, come in and ask to speak to Cath.

And it hardly needs adding, dear readers, that any more Jeffrey Woodworth CDs whose contents have now been transferred to your ipods would be greatly appreciated by Cath and the team at ABC!

STORIES...HAZEL MOSES.....

I didn't realise that people still gave names to their cars.

"Dear me, it's busy in town," Julia Yates had said breezily, removing a calf-length Jaeger coat beneath which lay a figure-hugging outfit. "It just gets harder and harder to find somewhere to leave Reggie."

And would you believe she's into fucking astrology? She even used it to manoeuvre herself into the position of Teddy's helper.

"It might take us quite a while to sort out the books," she explained, "as there are still so many unwanted Christmas presents coming in. Maybe it's just the Libran in me coming out, but I always like to approach my work in a balanced and harmonious way."

Teddy came over to my desk while I was writing my piece the following day.

"Crap name to give a charity, for the sake of an acronym," he said. "I've never been able to get used to the idea of battle as a transitive verb."

"That sounds just like the sort of comment my young sister would make," I said pointedly.

It's a pity that Teddy isn't better with women. Our Sally really was tailor-made for him. When he sees her picture in the paper next week it'll be a right eye-opener!

That Yates Lady, all over him like a rash, is bad news. She's a total outsider compared with the rest of them at ABC, despite a relentless charm offensive which leaves everyone cold.

"Oh, you look far too smart. You'll get muck all over that nice frock."

Cath had sounded more irritated than concerned when she saw Julia's fine, cream woollen shift, the sort of outfit most of us girls would wear on a night-out. Her make-up so was discreet you wouldn't have known she was wearing any; must have taken ages to apply. Come to think of it, Teddy was looking natty in a bottle-green sweater that I'd never seen before. One from Santa, probably.

Julia's a right little name-dropper. She just had to tell me that she knew Jeffrey Woodworth from Hereford University folk club; but then looked for some mysterious reason as if she regretted bringing this up.

Barbara knew Woodworth's hit single, Tory Lady in Red and she speculated, as everyone does, about the identity of the subject.

"Some folk reckon it might have been Fergie," she said.

"The football manager?" I said.

"No the Duchess of York, silly," Barbara said.

I thought that was only marginally more likely. The song opens along the lines of: "I met her at a folk club in the West Country/she was cool, she was lofty and she had no time for me."

"What do you think, Julia?" said Barbara.

"I've really no idea at all," she replied snootily, and we all fell into silence.

"Perhaps you would like to give Teddy a hand with our new books," Cath said to Barbara.

"Well, actually, I rather thought I could do that myself," said Julia, a little breathlessly, and then brought her star sign into the equation.

"If you like, Love," said Cath. In a charity shop it must be difficult to lay down the law if your staff can simply put on their fancy coats and walk away.

All the ladies had been pleased to see Teddy turn up, but none more so than Julia. Gavin did not exaggerate when he told me about Julia's gushing reaction to Teddy's generosity. Andy Dougan, however, was less thrilled by Teddy's presence and I suspect that Julia will be glad to see him moving on to that 'proper job'. Something's been going on there.

Julia was initially quite nippy on the stepladders in the stock room, despite her high heels, with Teddy holding the ladder to steady her. At one point, I sat down with a cuppa while Julia went up and down, giving Teddy a chance to admire her fine, gym-toned legs. But, poor lamb, Julia did begin to tire after a few journeys. She was forced to hold on to Teddy's shoulder as she came down; he, fortunately, raised no objection. On a later descent she landed a little unsteadily and fell gently towards him. Ha! Teddy's reaction to that foxy manoeuvre was an eye-opener!

I'd been hoping to have a good catch-up with Teddy. We're so overworked at the Gazette since last year's staff cuts (and more are on the way, I'm told) that we rarely have a chance for the chats we enjoyed on our days sitting together as sub-editors.

But I've never liked playing gooseberry, so I left them to it.

Julia was sporting a whopping wedding ring, like something from the Nun's Story. However, it didn't seem to worry either of them much, as they headed off for the pub together, without inviting me.

I think a word of caution in Teddy's ear is called for.

The National Diary

From our files

Kith and Kin

Do sons look for girls who are like their mother? Do mothers have excessively high expectations of their sons' girlfriends? For this week's Kith and Kin column, we spoke to Teddy Beresford and his mother, Valerie

TEDDY: As a teenager, I rarely brought girls home. I was worried that Mum would not approve. The funny thing was that my best friend, Henry Hawley, liked to invite girls home for precisely the same reason that I kept them away.

Henry was a bit quicker off the mark with the girls than I was. I wasted too much time thinking about my lost love, Rachel Waterfall. But Henry had lower standards than I did. "If you can't have love, you might as well try for a bit of sex while you're waiting for love to come along," he used to say. And that's where his mother's advice came into the equation.

Joan Hawley is a kind and warm-hearted woman, and I have remained in touch with the family since Henry died of leukaemia at the age of 23. But Joan had a tragic flaw. She was a devout churchgoer who believed that the fires of sexual passion should only be ignited after wedding bells have rung. Sex before marriage was, quite simply, wrong. This gave Henry and his mum an equally compelling obsession with his girlfriends' moral fibre, though for entirely different reasons.

Joan could tell within five minutes of meeting a girl whether she was 'nice' or not and she was unable to help herself from sharing this information with Henry. It was all in the tone of her voice, and even the occasional facial twitch. So Henry never wasted time on lost causes – the nice girls were quickly relegated to good-friend status. Henry was a skilful operator; few, if any, of the nice girls bore him a grudge, and several of them wept copiously at his funeral.

In my 20s, more of my girlfriends made it to meet Mum and Dad, and some proved to be palpable hits, particularly an Italian science student called Antonella Conte, whom I'd met in Rome. Mum even spoke highly of girls I wasn't too keen on myself. I think that, as I approached 30, an element of desperation was creeping in. Would I ever be off their hands? Would I ever get married?

Girls would sometimes say to me, after their first visit to my parents' house: "It must be funny, being shorter than your mother." It was one of those things that annoyed through repetition, and maybe because you'd been hoping that a girlfriend would at least have a veneer of sophistication and say something smarter or more original.

I suppose it is unusual, not being as tall as your mum. In my case, Dad's two inches shorter than I am, and I'm two inches shorter than Mum. It's certainly true that I like taller women (though you take every case on its merits, naturally) and Mum's a strong character. I've no time for wallflowers; I like my women to have a bit of chutzpah.

VALERIE: When Teddy was 15, I unearthed a few straightforward, hetero pornographic magazines from among his football programmes. I was relieved to learn that his tastes were so conventional, as Teddy's reticence where girls were concerned briefly made me wonder if he might be gay. I wouldn't have loved him any less and it might even have made me more protective, knowing that his life would be that much more difficult. For me, the worst thing you can say about homosexuality is that it's inconvenient.

Teddy always had very low expectations of where his life might lead and of what he might achieve. I never really understood where this lack of confidence came from, as he was nice looking, clever and good at sport. I don't suppose that going to an all boys' grammar school helped but plenty of lads who were in the same position managed all right, such as Henry Hawley, the lovely young man who died of cancer.

When Teddy was a teenager, he could make the girls laugh but he'd never move in for the kill, as it were. He'd say: "I think so and so is seeing someone else." Or: "I don't think I'm quite her type." I'd say: "Well, if you don't ask, you'll never find out, will you?" Then he'd go off in a huff as if I'd said something stupid.

I realise now that he had an almost pathological reluctance to open up to his mother on the subject of girls. I'd occasionally throw in a controversial remark about boy-girl relationships, just to get some kind of response out of him. Once, I even used the line favoured by Henry's mum, Joan, about many nice girls not wanting to sleep with boys before they were married.

I expected that would bring a response such as: "Get a life, Mum, this isn't the 1950s anymore," but Teddy just said: "You might have a point" and changed the subject. I began to wonder if I'd given birth to someone who was destined for the priesthood. I now realise that it was embarrassment over his lack of experience.

It's true that Philip and I have met quite a few of Teddy's girls down the years. But no one was ever quite right for him. What worries me now is that he seems to have given up on the idea of looking for a serious, long term-relationship in favour of flings that are devoted almost exclusively to short-term sexual gratification. Almost like he's making up for lost time, like Philip's constant craving for curry, which he never touched until he was 50.

We haven't said anything to Teddy – he is 33 when all is said and done – but I've had to bite my tongue once or twice over some of his less suitable attachments, and I don't know how I'm going to react next time it happens. The trouble is, how do I intervene without making matters worse? You think you know your own son better than anyone but his suicide attempt, which only failed because two friends were so worried about him that they came round and found him in time, rocked us to our very foundations. We didn't have the slightest idea that he was so vulnerable.

Teddy was an only child. Philip was a restraining influence on me but I certainly over indulged him somewhat. If he were now to get involved in any unsuitable relationships, telling him to walk away would not be easy.

CULL VALLEY EVENING GAZETTE

Saturday January 3 2009

Find out what the stars have in store for you with our astrologer, Mystic Chris

ARIES:

This has been a barren time for someone of your romantic disposition.

But things could be about to change thanks to a rare alignment of Venus and Mercury which will pave the way for a one-off opportunity. Take it now or live to regret it. Your lucky colour: red.

LIBRA:

Seek more simplicity and harmony in your life. You are, when all is said and done, a Libra. A friendly face will offer great prospects for really enjoying life to the full. Don't play hard to get or you could miss out on this vibrant and passionate new arrival on the scene. Your lucky colour: green.

STORIES...TEDDY.....

Our editor, Mark McClair, sees himself as a man of the most elevated principles, prepared to fight for the moral high ground.

McClair was very keen to get rid of the astrological column when he arrived at the Gazette. He was especially horrified to learn that, as in the Daily Reflector, 11 digits appeared after each star sign, giving people the opportunity to call this number at great expense and find out more.

He wasn't prepared for the backlash to his master plan to shepherd the Valley's residents out of the Middle Ages. Even Chuck Thrower gave it to him straight: "You know it's crap, and I know it's crap, Boss. But it's the first thing my daughters read. You've just got to have an astrological column, even if it's only an in-house job."

McClair backed down and the job defaulted to the latest editorial assistant. At least no one is being ripped off now by a charlatan with a premium rate telephone number.

Our current stargazer is delighted when someone offers to take it off her hands for a week or two, and I've always been happy to help out. I think that 'vibrant and passionate new arrival on the scene' sums me up nicely enough.

The National Diary

January 2009

Review: Quintessence of Dust, Henry Hawley (Idlewild, £7.99)

The persistence of memory

Teddy Beresford is enchanted by a brilliant first novel

Two years ago, Henry Hawley was acclaimed as a comic genius when he won the William Hill Sports Book Prize. *Wingers and Whippets: A History of Yorkshire Football* was both funny and touching, and few people reading Hawley's chapter about Tommy Taylor, the former Barnsley centre-forward who died in the Munich Air Disaster, could have failed to shed a tear.

The Beautiful Game plays a prominent role in *Quintessence of Dust*, which tells the story of three unhappy individuals, living in different countries, who all feel a single incident has marred their life.

Split-born footballer Darko Martinovic, then considered one of the game's most promising young talents, was dropped from the 1962 Yugoslavian World Cup squad following a fight with two team-mates from Belgrade; Scottish hairdresser Fiona McDonald's beloved father died suddenly of a heart attack when she was four years old; guitarist Greg Hinkle's world imploded when he was replaced in a rock band just before their big break. This trio has never met but their lives are inter-connected in ways that are soon to become apparent, and which will help them to move on and ultimately find happiness.

One of Hawley's major themes is the persistence of memory. What we choose to remember and what we let go can have a huge impact on our outlook, our happiness and, ultimately, even our sanity. *Quintessence of Dust* will strike a chord with anyone who has waited in vain for the phone to ring, or who has looked back on a life marred by too many wrong turnings.

Hawley has produced a first novel that can be enjoyed equally by both men and women. For all the references to football and rock music, and the vaguely anorak-like obsessions of Greg Hinkle,

Quintessence of Dust is a love story. The path of true love never ran smooth but, as Hawley observes, happy endings can come from the most surprising of sources.

It will be fascinating to see what roads this major talent chooses to drive down next.

CULL VALLEY EVENING GAZETTE

Friday January 16 2009

Quick off the mark

Women's page editor Hazel Moses thought speed-dating sounded like fun. But she's married – so she sent younger sister Sally Merrens, a midwife, along to an event in Hexroyd

I think it was Oscar Wilde who said that only a shallow person doesn't judge by appearances. Perhaps, seeing he was so sure that you could sum up somebody in the twinkling of an eye, he'd have liked speed-dating.

Time is not on the speed-dater's side; you get just a few minutes in which to impress a man or woman you've never met before. That might well have worked for Oscar, with his insight into human nature and his piercing wit. But the rest of us fumble around, desperately seeking common ground, and things to say that aren't totally trite – while looking across the room at a more interesting candidate and hoping that he or she isn't mesmerised by someone else before we can stake our claim.

At Cellar Vie wine bar in Hexroyd, assistant manager and speed-dating organiser Dominique Deschamps likes to create a party atmosphere. It worked for some but took me back uncomfortably to adolescence. It was like a school disco with the boys (no fraternisation allowed before the start) hanging around separately from the girls before somebody decides to make the first move.

Dominique called us all together to explain the rules after we'd all had a complimentary glass of wine or beer to soothe our nerves. And, yes, some of the girls I talked to before we went into battle were nervous. So was I, midwife turned fearless journalist for the evening!

My number one 'date' for the evening, let's call him Ross, was strikingly good looking, and didn't he know it. He liked books and films. "That's great," I said, then struggled to recall anything I'd seen recently at the pictures, even though I go quite often, other than a difficult South American film. I didn't do much better on books, and wasted a good half minute trying to come up with the name of something I'd read about a Dutch banker living in New York, who was mad on cricket. As if the actual title mattered!

Before we made much progress, Dominique blew her whistle, the signal for all the men to move to another partner. I thought back to school disco days again as another man, who I really didn't like the look of, approached me. Still, this is the where the three-minute time slot comes into its own. You're not stuck with someone for too long.

I did begin to enjoy myself more, although none of the boys was quite up my street and I reckoned that the feeling was mutual. Someone who liked rambling and 'folk/roots' music was pleasant enough although not my type. He knew rather more about Portuguese fado and Bulgarian women's choirs than was strictly necessary. Then again, he was talking to someone who couldn't remember the name of the last CD she bought.

Anyone who's tried speed-dating will surely be familiar with the equivalents of those nosy sightseers who look round houses purely to satisfy their curiosity. One irritating individual, a university student, even mentioned his other half. When I asked what he was doing here, he replied: "No harm in a bit of window-shopping, is there?" If he's reading this, he should consider himself lucky that I haven't grassed him up to his girlfriend by mentioning his name!

If you like someone, you tell Dominique and pass on your contact details. If any couples match up, the information is forwarded to both parties after the event. Yours truly drew a blank in both columns, sad to say.

"Any happy-ever-after stories to tell me about?" I asked Dominique, who has been running these occasional speed-dating sessions for a year, after we'd wound up.

"A couple in here recently did tell me that they met through us. On the night, there's occasionally a pair who you can see are hitting it off immediately. It might be obvious through their body language or a farewell gesture at the end of the three minutes which is clearly au revoir rather than goodbye! But probably not tonight," she admitted.

"You can never force these things but I like to think that we act as a catalyst for anyone seeking romance. If people don't find what they are looking for here, we will at least have encouraged them to carry on the search. I'm sure it helps to know that there are so many others in the same boat, looking for love."

I'm not sure that speed-dating is for me, although it was great fun to give it a try. Details of the next meetings are available from Dominique at Cellar Vie. It's essential to book in advance as numbers are limited and she wants to get an even M-F mix. And all the events are age-compatible – Dominique is planning her first over 40s' night in August.

Stories they cannot print

SALLY MERRENS

One of the Gazette reporters – Jeannie Derby, a friend of Hazel's although I've never met her myself – cried off that assignment at the last minute, saying it wasn't really her thing. I was up from London, visiting my sister, which is why I stepped in.

"If you can manage around 800 words, that'd be great, and you never know your luck, Mr Right might be awaiting you," said Hazel.

She's gone native in Yorkshire, and I'm considering a move myself; you can do midwifery anywhere. Hazel once suggested that I'd get on like a house on fire with her friend Teddy Beresford. "Some rough edges but you could sort him out, in the nicest possible way," she said.

We'd planned a foursome with Hazel and Jim. It never happened because Teddy did an 11th-hour Jeannie Derby and ducked out. So much for this northern grit they tell me about.

"Is it all right?" I asked Hazel, the day after she read my piece.

"I've tinkered with it a little, for house style and things, but it's fine," she said, "and Teddy thought so too, for what it's worth."

Hazel had actually rearranged quite a few things in my article. I'd started off by introducing Dominique, but she said my Oscar Wilde line was a better one for the "intro," as she called it, and she also removed one or two of my more whimsical observations. "Some people lose interest before you've even opened your mouth," I wrote. "I'm quite tall, and one little guy smiled to himself as he sat down, as if it were his chance to have a few minutes 'off'. As it happens, I can't see what possible odds it makes whether a bloke is a few inches shorter than a girl."

On the night, I'd thought 'Ross', a film buff, might be impressed that I'd seen a Chilean movie.

"Tony Manero," I said, after a struggle with the title. "Quite interesting."

"The one about the serial killer?" he said, looking alarmed at my taste.

"Yes," I said, because there was no denying that that's what it was all about.

"Was there much about politics in it?" he said, perhaps trying to help me to come up with a more savoury reason for finding the film good.

"There were a few references to the coup against Pinochet."

"Oh. Allende, you mean."

"Of course, I always get those two mixed up."

"I suppose it's easy to confuse a fascist dictator and a democratically-elected socialist leader."

"I mix up the names, I mean, I understand the politics, you patronising git," I should have said.

Then I got stuck on the name of that cricket novel – by Joseph O'Neill, I remembered too late – Dominique's whistle blew, 'Ross' smiled patronisingly and the boys all moved along the bus, so to speak.

The rest of the men didn't even look enticing.

"D'you get to clubs?" someone asked me.

"No," I said.

Does Leyton Orient count?

"As you're a right gangly lass and I'm a shortish bloke, I guess we've both got a similar problem."

I bet you're in proportion too.

"I always thought Dogme 95 was a sexual position."

Can't see any women offering you the opportunity to find out.

"Never thought a lass would like Golden Accelerator."

Never thought so many blokes would drink that American shit straight from the bottle.

"Aren't you a bit old to be living with your parents?"

Aren't you a bit old to be asking such socially-inept questions?

"What are you driving at the moment?"

What possible interest could I have in answering such a spectacularly banal question?

I can't remember when I bit my tongue so much; I guess I'm just terminally polite.

So: if you had to summarise the sort of bloke I'm looking for, he'd be someone who is nice looking, height pretty much immaterial as long as he's not a midget, likes decent pubs and real ale, hates night clubs, has a sense of humour, reads books, doesn't care for cars, is thoughtful or at least capable of being so if properly house-trained by me, imaginative, enjoys trips to lower-division football matches, theatres and cinemas.

Where the hell are you going to find someone with all that going for them?

Advertisement Feature

(Draft copy only, FAO Teddy Beresford)

Shopping locally in Hexroyd and Ainsley

How well do you know your own patch? The American writer Emerson said that he had travelled well in Concord, a statement which admittedly reads rather differently now than it did in the 19th century.

Here in the Cull Valley, we are blessed to live in one of the most beautiful parts of the North. The nearby countryside is spectacular and people travel from throughout England to visit Greenwood Crags, which is especially gorgeous in spring and in the season of mellow fruitfulness. A tributary of the River Cull runs through the Crags and some magnificent woodland remains a refuge, from their predatory, ugly grey American cousins, for our lovely native red squirrel.

The towns of Hexroyd and Ainsley are just six miles apart, but bustling and energetic in fascinatingly different ways. Big brother Hexroyd is home to one of the UK's biggest building societies, which occupies fine glass-and-concrete premises in the centre of the town.

But Hexroyd hasn't turned its back on the past and a notable feature is the eighteenth century Wool Hall, no longer associated with that industry, of course, but now converted into an open-air market of colonnaded galleries which is home to dozens of independent traders. Elsewhere in the town, make sure that you also see the Clegg Textile Museum and the 15th century parish church with its fine stained-glass windows.

Now we travel along the A8814 on that short trip to Ainsley. Careful as you go, by the way: there are regular calls for new barriers and speed restrictions on this winding road through the valley, which has claimed a few lives.

Little brother Ainsley, close to the boundary with Lancashire, is an old cotton town and there's always been a rivalry with Hexroyd. It's usually been a healthy one, too, give or take a few scraps every Saturday night and the occasional skirmishes in the less salubrious resorts of Spain and Greece when Hexroydians and Ainsleyites, find themselves on the same package holidays.

There are, of course, a handful of Hexroydians who like to call Ainsleyites 'Schizos', because they can't quite make up their minds whether they are Yorkshire or Lancashire. But some Ainsley people actually came from Manchester, London and the South-East in the 1970s, bringing sophistication and sometimes unconventional lifestyles to the area.

Perhaps the Cull Valley's biggest sense of community lies in the way that Hexroyd and Ainsley folk use each others' shops. Both towns have a high percentage of independent outlets, and although Hexroyd has its fair share of high street names, they don't proliferate as they do elsewhere. The important thing is that everything is available on your doorstep if you live in Hexroyd or Ainsley.

In both village and small-town France, the boulangerie and patisserie still hold sway. In Ainsley, long-established specialist shops such as Hopkinson's Family Butcher's continue to prosper, safeguarded by the continuing loyalty of a new generation of customers.

There will naturally always be sporting rivalry. Fans of Hexroyd Park Avenue mock the smaller town for its lack of a Football League side. Ainsley Athletic was voted out of the old Division Four in 1965. The club now plays in the Unibond Premier Division.

Where Ainsley does score over Hexroyd, however, is in having its own Nobel Laureate, Sir Noel Armstrong. He, of course, discovered what is now known as 'The Armstrong Effect,' the law of physics which states that if all the molecules in a solid object shift in precisely the same direction at precisely the same moment, that object will move of its own accord.

Your motor car, for example, could theoretically move out of your garage on to the driveway of its own accord, like an eager puppy telling you that it wants to go for a walk. But scientists do admit that it's a highly unlikely occurrence. There are plenty of good garages in the area if you do need to seek out a motor vehicle specialist.

If you've not allowed yourself a close look at Hexroyd and Ainsley recently, take a leaf out of Emerson's book and go local. You'll find all the business and services you could possibly need on your doorstep.

From: Edward.beresford@univalleypapers.co.uk
Date: 9 January, 2009 15:00
To: Stanley.cartwright@univalleypapers.co.uk
Subj: No sodding movement here, Pal!

I am a long-standing resident of the Cull Valley, and I do not need to be lectured by you, Mr Stanley Winston Cartwright, in my local newspaper (Advertisement feature, Shopping locally) regarding the places I have known and loved all my life.

Neither am I sure of the purpose served by reminding people about the mindless rivalry between the young people of both towns. Every summer this besmirches the names of Hexroyd, Ainsley, Yorkshire and England in the minds of Spanish and Greek citizens.

I was also baffled, incidentally, by the reference to the Armstrong Effect. I remember a similar joke going the rounds, regarding molecular movement, during my physics GSCE days at West Pennine Grammar. The notion that someone called Sir Noel Armstrong received the highest accolade that the scientific world can bestow for this 'theory' had me checking the top of your journal to make sure that it was not April 1.

Yrs, Teddy

From: Edward.beresford@univalleypapers.co.uk
Date: 9 January, 2009 15:05
To: Stanley.cartwright@univalleypapers.co.uk
Subj: The wrong American
BTW, Stan, wasn't it Thoreau, rather than Emerson, who said: "I am well traveled (US spelling, please note) in Concord?"
(Advertisement Feature, Shopping locally in Hexroyd and Ainsley).

Stories they cannot print

STAN CARTWRIGHT....

How did it come to this? Shopping locally in Hexroyd and Ainsley with Stan Cartwright.

When Teddy tells me he's the sub-editor who will be reading my copy, we amuse ourselves harmlessly with a game of Call My Bluff. He has to spot the facetious bits that need taking out, and the apparent flights of fancy that are actually correct. Teddy's a hard man to catch out.

Yes, we do have a laugh, but I know it troubles him to see me reduced to the role of editorial Untermensch; all the more since I'd been his mentor. When Teddy had got a couple of years' experience as a reporter under his belt, I said to him: "Don't stay here for ever. I know you're a local lad but you don't want to end up like me or Reuben Parfitt."

"Not Parfitt, maybe, but I'd settle for your job one day, Stan."

A fair point, I suppose. I was news editor in those days. Maybe I had some inkling of the grim way that things would pan out later. As for Reuben Parfitt, he was this sad cove with a control-freak wife. He was only in his late 50s, though he looked much older, and he'd been part of the Gazette furniture for a good 30 years. He had a funny, gallant little way of smiling ingratiatingly when one of the "lady reporters", as he called them, went past. "A Parfitt gentleman," we used to say. He could do everything a bit, but nothing very well, and no one was ever sure what to do with him. Shortly after a reshuffle put him under my jurisdiction, Mark McClair finally decided that it was time to hand Parfitt the P45.

McClair had arrived three years earlier from a national, tabloid newspaper. "My door will always be open," he reassured the nervous, assembled team. McClair had come with quite a reputation; "He gives megalomania a bad name," a reporter heard via a friend at the Daily Reflector. After a couple of weeks in the editor's chair, McClair's door closed quite literally and you knocked with considerable trepidation before entering. The moment you stepped inside, the world was a darker place. McClair was a black hole, sucking in all his subjects' hope for the future; all fundamental laws of decency and fair play broke down entirely in his presence.

I was called to see McClair one Monday morning early in the new century. I steeled myself for the step beyond the event horizon.

"You wanted to see me, Boss," I said after I'd been green-lighted.

"Parfitt's got to go, Stan. He's not much cop and, anyway, he's creating a bad atmosphere," McClair said without preliminaries.

"Parfitt?" I laughed. "He's not great but he's as harmless and mild-mannered an individual who has ever walked through these hallowed doors."

"There have been complaints," continued McClair. "Some of the women don't like the way he leers at them. Sexism, you've got to be very careful about that sort of thing these days, Stan."

McClair, a thin-faced and perfectly bald man, superficially academic looking but with no discernible intellect, stared at me over his rimless spectacles. On the wall behind him was a mock front page to mark his departure from the Daily Reflector, and a framed and signed work by the Reflector's resident political cartoonist. It was something to do with cannibalism; most newspaper editors have no sense of humour or an unpleasant one.

"Couldn't we find something else for him, perhaps helping the librarians with some cuttings and digging out photographs, Boss." I hated referring to a 30-year-old as boss, but it was what he liked. "You're being a trifle harsh, maybe," I said cautiously.

"Harsh? Point A. This isn't a parish church magazine, you know."

"I'm aware of that, Boss."

"In any case, plans are afoot to make the library a self-service facility. Point 2. This is not a charitable organisation to prop up hacks who are way past their sell-by date."

"That is true also," I admitted. "Maybe we could at least keep him on part-time out of the bucks saved when the librarians go. I don't suppose anyone's told them?"

"We're not taking about the librarians. We're talking about Reuben Parfitt."

"Look, Boss, the chap's a bit slow. You couldn't trust him to handle the splash with the deadline looming, or to knock out a 1,000-word piece on the state of the NHS, but he's not actually a liability. And he's not, I understand, a high earner. Where's he going to get another job?"

"Which brings me back to Point B," said McClair, with a skeletal grin.

95

"I think you said it was Point 2, actually, Boss. So when are you going to tell him?" I asked.

"You should speak to him today, Stan," said McClair, who lowered his head, looked at me over his glasses and started to blink furiously; the warning sign, like a dog whose tail stops wagging, that his patience was wearing thin.

"With respect, Boss, I would have thought that was your job."

"No, you're his line manager."

"And you're the editor. The buck stops with you, it comes with the territory."

I stormed out of his office and slammed the door; not the wisest move I've made during my career.

CULL VALLEY EVENING GAZETTE

Monday February 26 2009

Jobless figures steady

Jobless figures throughout the Cull Valley have remained virtually the same during the last two months. The number of Jobseeker's Allowance (JSA) claimants rose by 10 to 5,216 in April. The previous month, the figure had gone down by eight.

STORIES...GAVIN LAYTON....

I had so much on my plate today that no news was good news on the unemployment front. Nothing there that I needed to pursue.

The previous week, we'd reported that a handful of jobs had gone at The Finney Press, a struggling printing firm in the centre of Hexroyd close to where the old Gazette office used to be before the move out of town.

"I've heard that Bob Finney is now thinking of calling it a day altogether, he's lost a good few contracts during the past 12 months. Wondered if I might use it as part of a feature about beleaguered small and medium-sized enterprises," I said to Teddy Beresford.

"It's a good idea but I can't see McClair being too keen on mentioning Finney," said Teddy. "He was one of the people responsible for pulling the plug on him. The Gazette used to sub-contract some jobs to Finney but that all stopped a while back. Great pity, there were a lot of hands working there at one time," he added, suddenly misty-eyed.

"You sound sad about that. What's the company to you?" I asked.

"They published an article I wrote about a coaching session with an Ainsley Athletic footballer," he said, "For the Badger Hill School Telegraph. Bob Finney was my teacher's cousin. And the dad of Tom Waterfall, the film man, worked for him on and off."

"That so?" I said. Not being a local lad – I'm from Rochdale – I wasn't always familiar with these connections.

"Tom was the editor of our little school paper; he was the brightest kid in the class. Funny thing is I was only thinking about that recently. When Bob Finney found out who was in charge of our publication he said: "That's nice to see, very pleased for you, Tom."

"Somewhat effusive response."

"Yes, and maybe a little patronising, too, but probably well meant. I only worked out the reason he said it much later. Tom's dad had died shortly before our visit, and Bob Finney must have remembered him as one of the, shall we say, more laid-back employees. He'd have been amused to see that young Tom was a different type altogether. You only had to meet him for a minute to see that he had more about him than his dad. Lackadaisical was the word Tom used about his old man."

"That's quite a big one for a primary school kid."

"He was full of them. We used to ask him if he'd swallowed a dictionary."

I wanted to know if a way with words had helped Tom Waterfall to win the hand of that lovely wife. But something I'd heard from Hazel and Jeannie made such an observation inadvisable.

The National Diary

From our files

'My first story'

The column in which journalists reveal how they cut their teeth. This week's guest writer, sub-editor Teddy Beresford of the *Cull Valley Evening Gazette*, recalls a lesson that stood him in good stead

During my time at the University of Devon, I worked on the student newspaper, *South-West Side Story*.

I did some proof-reading and reviewed plays and minor gigs that the more established members of the editorial team didn't fancy. One rag week, I was given my first decent job, to write a 'colour piece' about a charity auction. Some cartoonists had donated work, and there were a few big names including Posy Simmonds, Bill Tidy, and Maurice Dodd and Dennis Collins, the men who did *The Perishers* in the *Daily Mirror*. Reserve prices ranged from a tenner to £50.

Only two or three items into the auction, we were disrupted by a drunken tramp with a messy beard. He kept shouting down the auctioneer with idiotic bids. The auctioneer gave up and we were invited to make our bids to the rag office the following morning.

My brain must have been in neutral that evening. At one point I was standing right next to the 'tramp'. I moved away because he kept scratching himself somewhat theatrically, but I never stopped to ask myself why he smelled as fresh as a daisy, with a hint of expensive cologne. Instead, I went to the bar, had a few beers and forgot about the whole business.

All hell broke loose the next morning. There was such interest in the cartoons that a big queue formed outside the rag office at 8-30, a remarkable achievement for a bunch of students. The office was empty. When a couple of rag committee officers finally opened up two hours later, they claimed that all the cartoons had been sold.

A few inquiries by *South-West Side Story* revealed that the tramp was a student planted by the rag committee, who had then divided up the best cartoons for the reserve price. The story got into the local evening newspaper and, because the rag committee chairman was the son of an MP, made the nationals too. My suggestion to Stan Cartwright, the *Cull Valley Evening Gazette* news editor, that I'd been part of the team who uncovered the scam was not, therefore, entirely accurate.

But I learned a few lessons, and they have served me well in journalism. *Don't take things for granted. Be sceptical. Be prepared to do a bit of digging.* During a week of work experience at the *Gazette*, I was sent out to cover a golden wedding. On the way back I saw some dairy workers standing round a brazier. As a child of the Thatcher era, I was too young to associate braziers with strikes. But I thought about how I'd missed the charity scam, and decided that I'd stop to see if something important was going on. I think I had a vision of people ringing the newspaper to tip them off, and Stan Cartwright saying: "You must have driven past that, lad, the dairy's on the route. Didn't you see anything?"

So, my first story as an adult, the one at university, wasn't my first story; it was somebody else's first story. Much as Rachel Waterfall, my first girlfriend, wasn't my first girlfriend; she was somebody else's first girlfriend – and wife, as it later transpired.

At least I turned out to be better equipped for writing newspaper stories than I ever was for dealing with women.

CULL VALLEY EVENING GAZETTE

Classifieds
Saturday August 22 1970
SECOND-HAND MOTOR CARS

Bright-red 1966 105E model Ford Anglia, one careful owner. Immaculate condition and low mileage, £375 ono.

Julia's Journal

Robbie Santiago's gone back to London, good riddance after the way he treated me. Thank heavens that I've definitely got lovely Teddy lined up, though the two are hardly comparable. Robbie was just a fling but Teddy, well, he could be something quite different. I've been thinking about what I wrote yesterday, about Teddy being just what I'm looking for.

It was really meant as nothing more than a throwaway comment. But you've been kidding yourself, Julia. You have been in denial. And what have you been in denial about? Come on, Lady, spit it out. You have been in denial about babies. All that talk about how much you disliked them, and how you wouldn't want to be tied down by a puking, wailing little monster; the feigned indifference when someone brings a baby into the shop and all the ladies, and even Andy and the wet widower, are cooing over it.

Last year that wouldn't have been a million miles from the truth. But it's right what they say about the biological time clock, after all. Who'd have thought I of all people would have succumbed? And who would have thought that Teddy would come along at the right moment?

Step one is to lure your man, and things went very well in the shop today; the first hurdle has been crossed effortlessly. By which I mean that there are not going to be any problems in Teddy's trouser department. I'm married to a man who wouldn't be aroused if he was sucked off by Helen of Troy. That does make it rather delicious to meet someone who is the victim of a below-the-belt commotion when you fall into his arms from a stepladder. In an ideal world, we wouldn't have had the Wandering Jewess prowling round the building and trying to get in on the act when Teddy and I decided to go off to the pub after work. But she got the message that she wasn't welcome.

When Teddy and I were chatting in the Masons, he was at great pains to point out that he was going to be in again the following Wednesday "and not Tuesday", because of his job. It was very sweet the way he emphasised the "not", to make sure I'd got the message, then blushed — bless! — because of what he was implying.

"I might have to change to Wednesday myself, because of other commitments," I said, to assure him that he was coming through loud and clear. When I returned from the ladies', I sat a little closer to him than I'd been before, and he liked that well enough.

Cath Wilson nearly messed things up in her usual fashion by saying that I'd be far more use if I stuck with my Tuesday shift. But Barbara Machin played ball when I called her at home.

"It's Julia from the shop. Can you help me out," I said. "I wonder if you could be very kind and do me a big favour. You'd really be helping me out of a fix."

"Of course," Barbara said, without hesitation. Bless. Then something occurred to her.

"Oh, I had been hoping to have a word with Teddy on Wednesday."

How corny is this, but my heart skipped a beat.

"Teddy?" I said, in an off-hand manner. "Oh, yes, of course."

"Yes, Teddy. I think you should be able to recall him if you think back very carefully. Wasn't he the one you went to the pub with?" The sarcastic cow.

"I'd been hoping to have a word with him on my grandson's behalf, you know the one I told you about, who's interested in going into journalism," she added. "But I dare say that it'll keep to another time."

"Thanks, Barbara, you're a pet. I'll mention that to Teddy and I'll look after him. We want to keep him sweet, don't we?"

104

"Of course we do. And I'm sure that you're the right person for the job, Dearie," Barbara replied. I didn't like the tone of voice one little bit.

CULL VALLEY EVENING GAZETTE

Monday December 14 1998

Valley mourns talented student

By Stan Cartwright

A gifted young postgraduate student from Hexroyd has lost his battle against cancer.

Former West Pennine Grammar pupil Henry Hawley, aged 23, was diagnosed with leukaemia last summer, shortly after he graduated with first-class honours in Modern Languages from Durham University. He died yesterday, with his family by his side, three days after being admitted to St Andrew's Hospice, Hexroyd.

His parents Bert and Joan Hawley, said: "Henry put up an incredible fight throughout his dreadful illness. He was quite simply an inspirational young man and the most wonderful son, and brother to his three sisters. We'd like to thank everyone who cared for him, including his great friends who helped to keep his spirits up and with whom he never stopped smiling until the end."

Last September, Henry began an MA in Italian Cinema at Leeds University, while undergoing chemotherapy treatment, but was forced to give up his studies.

As an undergraduate, Henry had supplemented his income by selling topical jokes to radio quiz shows, and he had already succeeded in having several articles and contributions accepted by national magazines, including *Private Eye* and *The Oldie*.

Cull Valley Gazette journalist Teddy Beresford, one of Henry's closest friends since school days at West Pennine Grammar said: "Hank, as we called him, was one of the nicest guys you could hope to meet as well as one the cleverest and the funniest. I felt privileged to be a family friend, and I felt sure he was destined for great things. It's a terrible loss."

The funeral will take place at Eastlands Methodist Church, Hexroyd, on Tuesday, December 22 at 11am.

The family has requested no flowers. Donations can be sent to Ainsley Against Cancer.

STORIES...STAN CARTWRIGHT....

It was very hard speaking to Teddy about the death of his friend. I don't ever think that I've seen him so downhearted. Henry Hawley was clearly an impressive young man.

I did meet him, just the once, after a Hexroyd Hornets rugby league match. Jim Stafford, the sports editor, and I went into the pub for last orders. Teddy and Henry, who had also been at the game, were there. I bought a round and we joined them.

It was immediately obvious that they had one of those close male friendships, the right side of laddish, that I had always envied. I never had any really good mates after leaving school, mainly because I got married so young and was a dad before I was 21. The trouble is, I didn't win that one at the other end of the parenting game, by bagging myself plenty of 'quality time' with my wife while my peers were still bogged down with the ghastly business of teenagers. I'm sure that some middle-aged couples with shed loads of disposable income, and the kids off their hands, head for exotic holidays in Peru, India and China and generally have the time of their life. But my wife Suzanne and I, sticking together as much through lethargy and because no one else would have us as for any other reason, were not a happy twosome. And we weren't even affluent empty nesters. Suzanne didn't work, and my Gazette income had never enabled us to get ahead of the game financially.

So there I was, sitting in the Swan and Cemetery with two bright young lads, just 21, who had their lives before them. They were both doing well with their studies. Henry was returning to Durham, following a year as a languages student in Caen and Verona, and Teddy was going to Cardiff on that postgraduate journalism course after getting an upper-second degree. At their age, I'd been chasing ambulances for the Cull Valley Gazette, living with a woman who was more wedded to our corner of West Yorkshire than she was to me, and knee-deep in nappies. Even then, my life was becoming set in concrete. But for Teddy and Henry, life's possibilities seemed infinite.

Henry, in particular, exuded the air of someone who knew this. Apart from a mass of Afro-like wavy hair, he was an unremarkable-looking youth of medium height. His round, John-Lennon style glasses complemented his friendly, square-shaped face and he seemed extraordinarily interested in hearing what Jim and I had to say. Mind you, all Park Avenue fans who supported the club in the late 1980s and early 1990s, and who read Jim's reports, are delighted to meet him.

Teddy and Henry had this way of picking up daft ideas, chewing them over and taking them down ever more surreal paths. That night the conversation turned briefly to morris dancing, which neither of them had much time for. I could see them hesitating over so easy a target, before deciding that they might as well have a pop.

Henry said: "Funny really, we're both real ale drinkers so I suppose morris dancing ought to be right up our alley."

Then Teddy, doubtless inspired by the Hornets' match, said: "Yes, but give me the kosher morris dancing union version. Not the watered-down 13-a-side League job."

Henry said: "Watered down? Our morris dancing leaguers make Ernest Shackleton and his merry men look soft. Don't forget that I were brought up on League, that's why I'm so rock-hard."

"Yeah, yeah," said Teddy, "Your great grand-dad was at the George Hotel in Huddersfield when the big split came with the Union boys in 1895. We've heard it all before, everyone claims they were there, making sure they got their share of the money."

"But it had to come," said Henry. "When you'd got 10 mouths to feed, you couldn't take time out from working as a treacle bender, without some form of compensation."

"And your dad," added Teddy, "I suppose you claim he set you on the right path, taking you to the Rose and Crown for your first fixture, before the posh school had a chance to convert you to morris dancing union...."

It was an equal partnership in which Teddy held his own comfortably; he was every bit as quick off the mark as Henry. However, I only thought about it in those terms much later, when I realised the extent to which Teddy had put Henry on a pedestal and assumed that his friend was the one with all the talent, the one who would make his mark on the world while Teddy himself would remain, like me I suppose, one of life's smaller fry.

The National Diary

Ask Jenny

Our agony aunt Jenny Dudley won't pull her punches

Dear Jenny – I'm a 33-year-old bachelor who still lives with his parents. In many ways, however, I don't fit the stereotypical image that will spring into everyone's mind when they read that sentence.

For a start, 'still' is misleading. I went to university in a city 300 miles from my home town and, for a couple of years in my early 20s, shared a flat with a colleague from work. When he got a job in London, I quit the flat and decided to buy a house. I moved back in with my parents while I looked round and, for one reason or another, stayed there. The three of us (I'm an only child) rattle around in this five-bedroom house. My parents both enjoy my presence – I've always had a good relationship with them – but despair of ever getting rid of me. They'd like me to meet a nice girl and, in the long run I suppose, give them grandchildren.

My immediate problem is a delicate one. I am desperate for regular sex. I've not had a serious relationship with a girlfriend for two years and my sexual frustration is driving me insane. I am sexually quite experienced; most often, my relationships have foundered because the women I met started to get too keen. I've always assumed that I would be able to commit to a long-term relationship with the right girl. But I've never met her; or at least, not since my teenage days.

I am presentable enough in appearance, some women even consider me good-looking, and I'm not an anorak. At least, I don't think I appear to be so; I keep my anorak-ish newspaper-style diary to myself. I have a wide range of interests, including reading, concert-going and travel. I have a respectable and quite satisfying job, not that well paid but more than adequate for my circumstances. So I have plenty of disposable income and I've never been mean with money.

As I say, I just don't seem to meet the right girls, although plenty of people have tried to lend me a helping hand. Hazel, a colleague and good friend of mine suggested recently that I might get on well with her sister. I decided to pass on that offer as match-making is usually a disaster, and it could be difficult if things don't pan out well. I'm too old for night clubs. Pubs I see as places for a nice pint of bitter, not for chatting up girls. In any case, I'm not extrovert and my 'qualities', such as they are, need to be teased out.

I certainly don't balk at the idea of paying to try my luck with a match-making agency. But I don't want to submit myself to the attentions of women who are trying something as a last resort. Two alternatives suggest themselves. One is to make regular visits to prostitutes, perhaps in a brothel, if anyone still uses that term. However, apart from the possibility of infection, I don't like the idea of exploiting women who might have taken to prostitution because of grim social circumstances, or who have to share their takings with some brutal pimp.

Alternative two is adultery, another road I have never gone down so far. One of my interests – book collecting and selling – has brought me into contact with the staff at a charity shop. One of the women there, a beautiful and, I guess, bored housewife is offering it to me on a plate, not to put too fine a point on it.

We've already been for a drink together, just early doors in a 'local'. At first I thought she was a flirt, but I was wrong. She has made it very clear that she wants to see me again, and I can barely contain my excitement. I've been asking around, I have found out a thing or two about her, and I've been fantasising about the form her strange home life, with a rich and probably gay husband, might take.

I had thought that this was too good to be true, one of the ultimate male fantasies: great sex on a regular basis before sending the woman home to her husband, no responsibilities and no questions asked. I'm trying to ignore a warning light that tells me she might just want something more from me, a new life and babies, even, which I'm not going to offer her. Because this is definitely lust, not love, for me.

I'm seriously tempted, although I know it would be wrong. What should I do, Jenny? Yours, Edward

Dear Edward – One of the things that fascinates me about dealing with readers' problems is their sheer diversity. Tolstoy said: 'All happy families are the same, every unhappy family is unhappy after its own fashion,' and it is true. No one has ever sent me a problem that replicates precisely a previous one, even though we can never escape from the familiar themes, whether it's abusive husbands, jealous wives or out-of-control children.

I've come across my fair share, too, of people like you – bachelors who, as middle age approaches, have not made the break from Mum and Dad. But I hardly know where to begin with your letter, not least because I don't know what to make of you. You see, Edward, going through readers' problems, I usually form a very quick impression of whether or not I like a person, but you are such an odd mixture that I don't know where I stand. One minute I want to hug you, and the next I think that I should throttle you. Are you quite a sensitive soul, or are you a curious amalgam of libertine and prim, as your reference to 'the possibility of infection' suggests?

Let's take all these points one by one. I've no way of knowing, on the basis of what you've told me now, whether there are serious issues in the past, but commitment is clearly a real dilemma for you. You don't seem to know what you want out of life. Will you, in ten years' time, regret not becoming a family man? Few people are fortunate enough to find a genuine soul mate and I do wonder whether you've let some nice girls slip through your fingers, simply because the initial, fierce passion has gone.

I'm irritated by your dismissal of dating agencies. Blind dates, by various means, have become far more socially acceptable in recent years. The notion that women must be drinking at the last-chance saloon, while men are just trying their luck, is arrogant, presumptuous and sexist.

Many people find a good partner through blind dates and some quite unconventional approaches are worth a go; you might try, for example, speed-dating. It only takes a second or two to establish whether you find someone potentially attractive and if you have sound antennae (though I'm not convinced that you have, Edward) you can pick up good or bad vibes reasonably quickly. Book dating has always struck me as an enterprising idea. If you discover that someone attractive is also a huge fan of a couple of your favourite writers, it's not a bad start.

But there are any number of ways a presentable 33-year-old, who isn't hampered by family commitments, can meet interesting people. Go to new places, always accept party invitations, try night classes. Yes, I can see you yawning over that old chestnut but you'll come across like-minded folk

Don't forget that, as a 30-something, there's a wide age range of women, younger and older, single and divorced, who might take your fancy and who might themselves be interested in you. I still think the world is your oyster; you've just got to be more proactive. I'm not saying that all these people will want to fall in bed with you at the drop of a hat, but many good things can come out of journeys along less-travelled roads.

What I *am* saying is that I'm not convinced this is just about sex, it must also be about a lack of tenderness with a member of the opposite sex. Look at your married friends. I'm willing to bet that some of them display a touching intimacy which everyone would love to experience. If it were merely sexual frustration, you could always get by, as I'm sure you do already, via the consolations of occasional masturbation.

Finally, and easily-offended readers might want to turn the page now, I don't think prostitutes should necessarily be ruled out if this *is* purely sexual. I shall, rather hastily, qualify that statement. Your attitude towards prostitution and the exploitation of women is precisely what convinces me that you do have a sensitive side to your nature. However, if you can find a high-class hooker of the kind who charges a three-figure sum for an evening's work and doesn't have to offload the majority of her earnings to a 'brutal (is there any other sort?) pimp', a prostitute in other words who is her own woman and is, arguably, exploiting men rather than the other way round, I see nothing intrinsically wrong with this.

It certainly sounds better than the brief fling with a bored housewife, as you put it, which you seem to be contemplating at the moment. And you say that it would be adultery uncomplicated by anything more serious. A woman who's in her 30s, a husband who's gay? That warning light should be heeded.

I think that sex is just the tip of the iceberg here. There are other issues and you need to decide very quickly what you want to do with the rest of your life or you will simply drift.

Let me know how you decide to handle this dilemma.

Yours, Jenny

CULL VALLEY EVENING GAZETTE

Wednesday February 11 2009

A Walk on the mild side

Drivers, I've got your number!

Our columnist and middle-aged fogey Kenneth 'Chuck' Thrower takes a light-hearted look at the way we live today, as he makes a Blurry-eyed effort to stay in tune with the youngsters, and says to personalised number plate owners: 'UR 50 VAIN'

I said to my teenage daughter, Claire, the other day: "I don't think today's pop groups are up to the stuff from the 1960s. It's just another example of what I'm always telling you – modern life is rubbish."

I didn't get the reaction I was hoping for. As you know, I am not averse to winding up the young 'uns. Indeed, a feature of life at Thrower Towers is my tendency to suggest that Fings Ain't What They Used To Be.

But instead of "Get real" or "Get a life," Claire said: "Nice one, Dad."

"What am I on about?" you ask, quite reasonably. Well, let me explain. Claire had been talking to her friend about the pop group Blur. One of their albums, apparently, is called *Modern Life is Rubbish*. Unfortunately, the blank look on my face when Claire praised me gave away the fact that, although I'd heard of Blur, I wasn't displaying the trademark wit that my regular readers have come to expect – I didn't even know the actual disc in question!

A strange way to start a column, you might be thinking, and you'd be right. It's the sort of filler anecdote with which you might expect me to wind up my weekly ramblings. Unfortunately, it's also the kind of thing that can get removed by the sub-editors – they are the chaps who read old Chuck's humble efforts and put a headline on them. They've got to make everything fit. The smarter subs, as they are known, will, through the judicious removal of the odd line here or there, make the column fit as snugly as a bug in a rug while retaining everything of significance. For the jobs-worth subs, however, it's far simpler, if in doubt, to simply take out a short item altogether, especially if they can throw in some excuse for doing so. I once came across a sub who deemed a columnist's joke non-PC. He removed it – no consultation, it just vanished, like an innocent victim of Soviet politics shoved into one of Uncle Joe's gulags.

Anyway, I'd like the Blur anecdote in, so I've brought it to the top of the page. It's safe, as Jim Bowen would say. Or at least I think it is. Let's hope this column starts with the words: "I said to my teenage daughter the other day…."

If, on the other hand, the opening words are "A strange way to start a column, you might be thinking, and you'd be right," we are well and truly up a gum tree.

Anyway, where was I? Oh yes, Modern Life is Rubbish. Nothing new there, Chuck, I hear you saying.

Fair point, dear reader, but every theme has plenty of variations for us to enjoy. You might, for example, reckon that there was nothing new to be said about that curse of our affluent society, the personalised number plate.

However, I've discovered an amusing way of irritating the ego-maniacs who drive around with these idiotic things attached to their bumpers. You might even like to try it for yourself.

It's in the way of things that these plates usually feature the owner's name. While visiting friends in leafy Cheshire, I spent an amusing few days greeting drivers as they emerged from their vehicles. "Hi, Tommy, or greetings Tracey," I'd say as the owners of a vehicle featuring the letters T-O-M or T-R-A-C emerged, adjusting their sunglasses to shield their eyes from the Alderley Edge sunlight.

"Have we met?" they'd say .

"North Cheshire Chamber of Commerce annual dinner," I'd say, or whatever nonsense I decided might fit the bill.

A bit of head-scratching follows. Tommy, Tracey or whoever looks a trifle exasperated, but more often than not he or she says that it's nice to meet up again and wishes you all the best.

There's always the danger of feeding their ego, you know, 'everyone knows who I am' sort of thing. But more likely, I reckon, is the chance that too much of this stuff will be a considerable irritant to the Tommys and Traceys and, even induce a touch of paranoia.

And it damned well should, Mr and Mrs Personalised Number Plate Owner. Because we are out to get you!

STORIES....KENNETH THROWER....

That number plate ruse doesn't always work out so amicably. I came across a driver the other day whose plates struck me as ripe for the Thrower treatment. He got out of his lovely racing green Lancia, and I nodded to him.

He returned my greeting politely, no doubt wondering where we had come across one another.

"Good morrow, Anthony."

"Er, hello. Have we met?"

"It's Kenneth. Was it the golf club?"

"I've never played golf, or been anywhere near a golf club."

"Perhaps it was the Mid-Pennine Chamber of Commerce annual dinner?"

"Hang on, hang on. Are you the journalist?"

"Journalist?" I said, cautiously. "A journalist, yes. Flattering description though it may be, I'm not so certain that I am the journalist."

"But you are not a Kenneth, are you? I know exactly who you are, and if this is your idea of a joke, it's not a good one. If you can't leave my wife alone, then at least be discreet."

Well, that's not the sort of invitation you get every day! Green light from the husband for some hanky-panky with missus. Problem is, he's got the wrong fella. I might not know much, but I do know I'm Kenneth, Chuck to friends. Who knows what that was all about? Pure paranoia.

Though come to think of it, I do know the identity of the man in the green car, and I should have recognised him as he's featured in the Gazette as a reasonably prominent local figure.

But I never got anywhere close to sleeping with his prick-teaser of a wife. Which does beg the question: who is the journalist, to whom he thought he was talking?

Julia's Journal

There won't be many easier conquests than Teddy.

"The Mason's?" he said, when I suggested a drink towards the end of his second afternoon with us at Ainsley Battling Cancer.

"Oh, I meant that I'd put the kettle on," I replied. As if.

I allowed him to look embarrassed for a few seconds.

"Well," I fluttered eventually, "The pub again. I can only have the one drink because of Reggie, but what a lovely idea."

So eight days later there we were again, back in the Mason's after a hard day's graft, away from those silly women. Like Barbara Machin who popped in this afternoon about her grandson, the aspiring journalist, and was put out because I'd apparently promised to say something to Teddy. Fight your own battles, Barbara.

Teddy is one of those real-ale men who consider the beer more important than the pub, but we had a very nice chat during which I sat very close to him and he crossed and uncrossed his legs a few times. He's a good listener, for a man, and he's observant, too. He spotted me scratching my scars, and he was very sympathetic when I explained about the childhood accident that had disfigured my left arm. Accident might not be quite the right word, but it'll do; that's all behind me now.

The Mason's is quite cosy as pubs go, but I told Teddy that the Cellar Vie wine bar was more my thing. He suggested that we might go together one evening and I said, quick as a flash, how about Sunday. His eyes lit up; I'd casually told him in the shop that Anthony would be going to London this weekend.

Is this a teeny bit forward of you, Julia? Perhaps. But there's no point in shilly-shallying.

I was surprised to learn that Teddy still lives with his parents. He was sheepish about that, rubbing his thumb nervously against his filtrum as if he were telling me a lie. I didn't miss the opportunity to advise him about those stylish new apartments in the old Barrowclough Mill. Prices are about 15 per cent down on this time last year, so it would be a very good time for him to get on the property ladder. Renting is dead money, I told him. "Arguably, though at least my cash is going into the not insubstantial family pot," he said.

"You don't want to think about it like that," I said.

We wouldn't want him to think that I was a gold digger, would we? Though it was something to bear in mind.

Well, the time flew by as we discussed this and that, and when I got home it was seven o'clock. I only beat Anthony by ten minutes, which just gave me time to freshen up and change into floaty chiffon, topped by the coral pink silk and cashmere cardigan he'd given me for my birthday. The sexy element is wasted on Anthony, but for all that he likes to see me wearing these things. It seems to fit some image of what he thinks married life should be like.

The oven had switched itself on three hours earlier and the smell of his favourite beef and bacon casserole was wafting through the house. Anthony was delighted. He went into the back of the utility room where he'd had a proper wine cellar built, and chose the Chateau Margaux which had gone down so well with the casserole last time. He handed me a stiff G&T while the wine breathed.

"Have you been slaving over a hot stove all afternoon?" he said.

"No I did it before I left. I've been into the shop, Barbara Machin asked me to swap shifts. She worked yesterday, I told you didn't I?"

"Did you meet anyone after work?" Anthony asked me.

He's not daft. Defensive responses to questions always make him suspicious.

"Yes, a journalist friend. We went to the Mason's, the one over the road from the shop."

"Is he local?"

"Why do you assume it's a he?"

"Isn't he a he?"

"Well, yes, he is, as it happens."

"Is he local, as it happens?"

"The New York Times. Of course he's fucking local."

"Well, I suppose you're due for one of your little affairs. There's no beating a bit of cock for putting a smile on your face."

"I've always understood that my heterosexual leanings are quite natural and healthy," I said. "Though they're not going to be satisfied round here any time soon, are they? "Anyway," I added in a moment of diversionary improvisation, before Anthony could react like John McEnroe to a dodgy line call, "I also met a lady journalist called Hazel Moses." He didn't need to know Hazel wasn't actually there today.

"And how would Hazel Moses fit into your exciting world?" Tony said, adopting that pompous, patronising tone in which he excels. "Isn't she the women's page editor of the Gazette?"

"That's right," I said. He must have known that because saintly old horse face had mentioned her. "I thought she might like to feature us in one of those Through the Keyhole articles, where they go into someone's nice house and show it to the readers."

"You didn't think you should have consulted me first?"

"Maybe I should. Sorry."

"I've no objections," he said. "As long as it doesn't involve me in any way, shape or form. Go ahead."

"Fine," I said, assuming that the male journalist had now been forgotten.

"But one more thing," he added, "I don't suppose for one moment that this fling is going to last any longer than any of the others. Just be discreet. I don't want people saying: 'That's the bloke whose wife is having it off with some local journalist.' That's not too much to ask, is it?"

"Of course not, Anthony," I said sweetly. "You're very understanding."

CULL VALLEY EVENING GAZETTE

Thursday October 9 2008

Film review: Holiday Stories (Cert PG)

A walk along the brigg

Jeannie Derby enjoys an impressive cinema debut by Cull Valley-born writer-director Tom Waterfall

As a young boy, Tom Waterfall enjoyed blissful summer holidays in the old-fashioned resort of Filey.

While other boys at his primary school were jetting off to Lanzarote and Disneyworld, young Tom Hogg (as he was at the time), and his parents Clifford and Betty, would get on the coach for the 50-odd mile trip to the Yorkshire coast, where his Uncle Len lived.

Fishing on Filey Brigg, and football and cricket on the beach provided Tom with some of the happiest days of his life. *Holiday Stories* focuses on three trips to Filey, in the early 1980s. The annual idyll ended abruptly in 1984, when Clifford Hogg died of a heart attack.

In his highly autobiographical debut as a film director and writer, Tom Waterfall has served up a wonderfully evocative noggin of nostalgia. Young Tom (an exceptional debut by 10-year-old Walter Sheringham) sees the world through the innocent yet knowing eyes of a young child.

It's clear that there are tensions between the playful, naïve Clifford (David Haig) and his younger wife, the tough and unsentimental Betty (Ann Marie Duff). In one scene, they argue about whether they can afford to buy young Tom a model aeroplane on which he has set his heart. Betty's views prevail and it's a moment given great poignancy by our knowledge that Clifford will be dead within the week, shortly after their return from the last ever trip to Filey.

This is a film which is short on plot but big on atmosphere. Waterfall, who worked in the advertising industry before making a BAFTA-nominated short film, is especially adept at capturing the personalities of the eccentric bunch who are regular visitors to his Uncle Len's bedsitter near the small resort, and who take Tom under their wing. The director is good, too, at creating the feel of a holiday resort which seems to be set in a time warp. For young Tom, it will stay that way for all time: we learn at the end that that there would be no more family holidays as Betty Hogg struggles to make ends meet.

An unhappy marriage provides more than a few passing clouds in *Holiday Stories* but the sunshine always emerges when Clifford and Uncle Len (Danny Webb) are on screen together. Waterfall can do both light and shade, and it will be fascinating to see which mood prevails in his next cinematic feature.

- Jeannie Derby's interview with Tom Waterfall: My debt to the Cull Valley, page seven.

STORIES....JEANNIE....

Rufus, the features man who writes on the arts, is on holiday right now. I almost said Rufus, our arts pages editor, but he's never been granted that fancy title; it might create the misleading impression that Mark McClair thought Rufus's job, or the arts in general, were somehow worth taking seriously.

Thrower is away, too, which is just as well. He'd probably have suggested that an interview with Waterfall would be up Teddy's street. I wasn't sure that he was strong enough to cope with that. Just as well that it ended up in my lap.

Hazel and I kept a close eye on Teddy the day the review and interview appeared. He turned straight to my review and then the interview, and consumed both in one big gulp, put the paper down and got on with his job. He was unusually quiet for the rest of the day, but he seemed to be okay. If he was thinking to himself: "That could have been me, having a nice family life with Rachel", he managed to keep it to himself.

And when Hazel casually suggested a quick beer before going home he agreed with no hesitation. He can't have been thrilled to read about the gloriously-fulfilled life of Tom Waterfall, but we really are sure that what happened earlier this year is now water under the bridge.

CULL VALLEY EVENING GAZETTE

Thursday March 5 2009

'I'll go to your house'

This month, women's page editor Hazel Moses takes a privileged peek through the keyhole, into the home of one of the Cull Valley's most glamorous couples

We've all, from time to time, seen a great property, put on what we imagine fondly to be our best strangulated Bostonian accent and said: "Who lives in a house like this?"

Well, I *have* known for a while that the modern Regency-style house on the hill in Green Pastures, one of Hexroyd's smartest suburbs, belongs to the architect Anthony Yates and his wife, Julia.

It's Julia who comes to the front door to greet me, a big, welcoming smile on her face. Together we pad across the parquet floor which covers the entire downstairs area, and I admire the bright colours in all the chimney recesses, contrasting so effectively with all the other brilliant white décor. The huge sofas, in primary colours, have been chosen to complement the recesses and there's a grandness about the place, too, with its elaborate lighting. The chandeliers must make dining here, as guests of Anthony and Julia, quite an event.

Above all, however, I am struck by how neat everything looks. When I left Casa Moses this morning, things were in their usual chaotic state – a pile of pots was waiting to be tackled, Jim's music and football magazines had taken on a life of their own and none of the reference books we'd consulted for a couple of crosswords had been returned to the shelves. But here in Green Pastures harmony reigns, everything is in its place. This might, I speculate, be for my benefit (that's not a criticism, needless to say, who wouldn't want to show a stranger a nice, tidy house?) and the Georgian proportions of most rooms play their part in creating a sense of order. Anthony and Julia don't seem to be burdened unnecessarily with what, for want of a better word, you might call 'stuff' or 'clutter'.

In the huge, shiny, white kitchen, all the worktops are empty and the appliances tucked away. There's a big bowl of fruit, all real apart from a ceramic pineapple in the middle. Two tasteful 'colourfield' pictures grace the living room walls, otherwise photographs seem to be more Julia's thing, and there are some fine black and white studies of the Cull Valley, as well as family shots.

Anthony has his own dedicated space, a large, book-lined study, containing an elegant desk and chair with Regency lines and proportions. He has also created a wine cellar recently, and it's fabulously well stocked by all accounts.

After viewing Anthony's study, it was up the generous staircase to the enormous master bedroom suite, where I discovered a tale of two archways. At one end, there's a bathroom and archway through to a dressing room for him, while at the other end a similar arrangement leads to a dressing room for her.

Julia has two shop window mannequins and uses them to try out combinations before deciding what to wear. As for her large collection of shoes, we laugh at my suggestion that it would only fail to impress the scorer if Imelda Marcos were keeping the tally! Julia's bathroom is the one place where her famed tidiness lets her down: a floor-to-ceiling glass-fronted cupboard is stuffed with cosmetics, lotions and potions, and everything here is slightly chaotic. What are her favourite brands? Just think of the most expensive: they're all here.

It's Anthony who's the tidy one in the bathroom, Julia tells me. All the wardrobes are closed, just a solitary trouser press in the corner.

The garden is an absolute delight, too, like something out of Chekhov, as I remarked to Julia. There's a revolving, wooden summerhouse in the middle of the lawn which must make this a blissful place to soak up the sun in flaming June (well, there's no harm in hoping!), July and August.

Anthony and Julia, incidentally, have a shared love of motor cars. Rather in the manner of a modern-day stables, there's a quadruple garage tucked away around the back to house their four vehicles, including Anthony's Lancia which he has had especially re-sprayed in British racing green. Julia has just taken delivery of a Mazda sports car, replacing her top-of-the range Golf, but she clearly has a very soft spot for Reggie, a perfectly preserved bright red 1966 Ford Anglia which she uses as her week-day run-around vehicle.

"We love our motors, and we love to travel but it's always great to come home," says Julia, before she waves me off.

124

STORIES....HAZEL...

Actually, I wasn't quite a total stranger being shown around the house. That ghastly, below-the-eyes grin vanished in a flash when I mentioned our previous meeting at the charity shop, and Teddy. Perhaps Julia thought I was delivering a gentle warning, and perhaps I was.

Tucked away in a dark corner of this horrible palace in Green Pastures there is a photograph of the happy couple on their wedding day. However, most pictures are simply of Julia in a variety of settings at home and abroad, sporting that fabulous, fabulous smile. A few images do feature a friend or relative but Julia is always centre stage in every picture.

Julia's dressing room doesn't disappoint. Kenneth Thrower was pleased to hear all about it. He closed his eyes, hands in pockets fiddling with his change, and he was no doubt imagining the scene: Julia sensuously removing her clothes and trying a new outfit from one of the mannequins, whose oddly twisted hands showed off some fine bracelets. I also told Kenneth how we laughed about our little Imelda Marcos exchange, though I don't think Julia was really that amused.

Julia did, however, appreciate my idea that the garden was like something out of Chekhov, though I was worried that I might have put my foot in it. "Little ones would love it here," I said, getting carried away because the summerhouse was so gorgeous. I couldn't read Julia as she absorbed that observation. She didn't strike me as the sort of person for whom children are part of the master plan, but who knows?

I was sorry not to have met Anthony, who remains for me a man of mystery, a face in the wedding photo: tall, dark and handsome in a way that manages to be both saturnine and a tad ascetic. He's away, I was told, at an architectural conference in London.

The driver of a Skoda Fabia, whom I spotted in a nearby lay-by, awaiting my departure, would have been less disappointed by Anthony's absence. Teddy had been a bit sharp with me when I brought up the subject of Julia.

"We're consenting adults and her marriage is on the rocks. I know that you mean well, and I'd never fall out with you of all people, but leave the interfering Emma Woodhouse act out of it, Hazel."

125

The National Diary

March 2009

Building for a brighter future

The Saturday Profile: Anthony Yates

Anthony Yates will never side with those people in his profession who view Prince Charles as an architectural dinosaur.

Yates, who returned from London three years ago to work in Hexroyd, West Yorkshire, believes that HRH's views on the state of contemporary architecture are "a breath of fresh air".

At the dinner parties he holds with his elegant wife, Julia, friends say he's not afraid to stick up for the old-fashioned architectural values of harmony and simplicity. Even the most iconic of modern buildings, such as Frank Gehry's Guggenheim in Bilbao, and Oscar Niemeyer's Brasilia Cathedral, receive short shrift from a man who is dedicated to the revival of past architectural glories.

These are views he is happy to share with everybody. For the *Cull Valley Evening Gazette*, the daily newspaper in his home town, Yates's pertinent views must be a godsend. He even kept up his subscription to the paper while living in London. Yates's pithy letters, ranging from the 'visual degeneracy' of most modern projects to anything that he deems offensive, offer more food for thought than the usual readers' fare about dog shit, wonderful amateur dramatics productions, and appeals for 1970s' speedway badges.

No one can accuse Yates of inconsistency. The Regency-style villa he designed himself and shares with Julia owes much to John Nash, even if it is somewhat out of character with the neighbouring five-bedroom/double garage detached properties in Green Pastures, the most affluent part of Hexroyd.

He's old fashioned in other ways, too. Church warden Yates has a reputation as something of a moral crusader. During his days working in London, neighbours in Muswell Hill were astonished that, during his long engagement to Julia, she would leave his house every evening to return to a flat that he had bought her, rather than staying the night.

A former neighbour once commented: "Anthony was always adamant that there would be no funny business before they got married. The institution of marriage is absolutely sacred as far as he is concerned."

Friends and relatives have been surprised that, so far, there is no sign of the patter of tiny feet. Five years after their marriage, it remains just the two of them in that Regency villa on the hill.

There's no shortage of disposable income Chez Yates. Julia cheerfully describes herself as "a lady who lunches", although she is to be seen twice a week helping out at a local charity shop, and both Anthony and Julia enjoy driving luxury-end motor cars. In Anthony's case, his Lancia even sports a personalised registration plate.

Anthony Yates was the son of a dinner lady and a bricklayer, both of whom had left school at 15. His father, Joshua Yates, had both ambition and talent. Night classes and day release study led to a Higher National Certificate in building and construction. Following foreman and site manager jobs with some big industry names, Joshua Yates went solo and built up a formidable reputation around West Yorkshire for his design-and-build projects.

The son, like his father, is a community-minded individual, and Anthony is the current deputy chairman of the Mid-Pennine Chamber of Commerce. In August, he will step up to the chairmanship of that organisation.

From a young age, Anthony, a Hexroyd Grammar School pupil, took a great interest in the growing family business. From his late teens onwards, it gave him ready-made summer vacation work while he studied architecture at Sheffield University.

"Anthony was never going to be a man for Inter-railing from Helsinki to Athens. As soon as we broke up for the summer, it was on with the hard hat and down to the building site," an old university acquaintance remembered.

His first few years in the profession saw him working mainly in London and the South-East, before he and Julia decided that the time was right to return to their Yorkshire roots. The move back north also provided the opportunity to rejoin the Cull Valley Shakers' morris dancing team of which Yates had been a founder member in his teenage years. His other interests include playing squash and watching rugby union, and he loves both fine wine and good beer.

Now, with Anthony on board, the projects handled by Josh Yates Builders are becoming more ambitious, although the son's innate conservatism makes it unlikely that the company will be picking up any gongs for innovation and cutting-edge work.

The local newspaper, meanwhile, will continue to benefit from Anthony's musings about the state of his profession, as well as any number of other local issues.

The Yates File

Born: Anthony Luke Yates, Leeds, April 10, 1969. He started life in a small, terraced house in the working-class district of Harehills.

Marital status: Married (in 2004) to Julia Lesley King.

Best of times: Graduating with first-class honours in architecture from the University of Sheffield. Winning, on two occasions, the Dancer of the Year award with the Cull Valley Shakers.

Worst of times: His honeymoon in the Seychelles.

Do say: Great dancing routine, Anthony. May I buy you a pint of Golden Accelerator?

Don't say: Is it true you are known as the Dancing Queen?

Beresford's Beat

Bad Santa gave me the creeps, says our columnist Teddy Beresford

I'll come clean. I never liked Father Christmas.

As a six-year-old, I had an unhappy experience with a Bad Santa in a department store; he smelled of beer and cigarettes, and told me I was a "spoilt little t**t" when I asked for an Adam Ant outfit.

That night I called my dad a "t**t", just to see how he would react.

"Where did you pick that word up?"

"Father Christmas."

"Any more jokes like that, and he won't be coming this or any other year."

On Christmas night, before I went to bed, I hid a picture of Mum, Dad and me. I was terrified that Santa would see it, remember me as the "spoilt little t**t" and leave nothing.

I was informed by Dad, a few weeks before the following Christmas, that Santa didn't exist. Mum was baffled when I gave a hearty cheer. I accept, however, that most kids have no problem with Santa, and that he's a harmless enough invention. But he really is just for the children.

The other week, I read a newspaper story about a local care home's Christmas entertainment. The manager said that the residents were all looking forward to seeing Santa the following day.

Well, I can tell you this for a fact, Mr Manager. The residents were *not* looking forward to meeting Santa. They have been fully aware that he is an imaginary person since the days when Grimsby Town and Brentford were playing in the top tier of English football. To treat them like little kids who are young enough to think that he can do every house in the world during one evening (working at an approximate rate of 0.0001 seconds per household is my estimate) has got to be the most stupidly patronising idea since, well, the last stupid and patronising idea in an old folks' home.

Let's face it, they're just old people. That's what you think, Mr Manager. You don't have to worry about their tastes or opinions, or when they were born. A friend of mine visited his great-aunt recently in a place where they were having a First World War sing-song. How old do they think these people are? Give them Glenn Miller, Cole Porter and Gershwin. Or Buddy Holly, Elvis and The Beatles.

I'm not a violent man and the last time I fought in public was at my old primary school, when some kid pinched my marbles. But if I ever find myself a resident in an old folks' home and I'm forced to sing *It's a Long Way to Tipperary*, or if I'm offered a chance to have a Christmas gift from Santa, I shall come out of retirement and I shan't be fighting by Queensberry Rules. I shall be chinning the home's entertainments manager, and I'll be doing it with the backing of all my fellow residents.

Care homes everywhere, you have been warned!

But in the meantime, a Merry Christmas to one and all.

STORIES....TEDDY...

I reminded Dad recently about my Santa phobia.

"I can't have been alone," I said, "I mean, who wants a tubby, bearded bloke puffing and panting around you in your bedroom?"

"Your mother's never minded," said Dad.

I braced myself for all hell to let loose after Bad Santa appeared. People telling me that I made up the story about Father Christmas; or suggesting that there's nothing wrong with forcing old folk brought up on Benny Goodman and Duke Ellington to sing songs from the First World War; or advising care home owners that I should be barred from taking up residence with them in my dotage.

Nothing of the sort: the only observation of any kind was made by Frances Jekyll, recently appointed chief sub-editor.

"You realise that I've got a seven-year-old great niece?" she said in the obscure and world-weary tone she adopted when she was gearing up for a pop at someone.

"Why would I know that, Fran? Pray come to the point."

"She still believes in Father Christmas."

"Ahhh. They're lovely at that age, aren't they?"

"But your column made it clear that he doesn't exist."

"She reads my column? What did she make of my views the other week on deconstruction and the modern novel?"

"Very funny. No, she doesn't actually read your column herself."

"Nothing to worry about, then."

"But some kiddie might."

"A brighter child, maybe. But I do take your point, and it won't happen again."

I could have added that the same day's paper contained three pictures of physically-differentiated Santas, which might equally have given the game away. But I'd already let my mouth get carried away with me, as it sometimes did when I spoke to Fran.

"Oh, by the way," I said, deciding to end on a more placatory note, "well done on your recent promotion."

I hoped my intonation sounded genuine, but I could tell she thought I was still being a sarcastic bastard.

Wednesday August 16 2006

Dr Mary's Surgery

Our no-holds-barred agony aunt and medical adviser examines your problems

Dear Dr Mary – I have just embarked on an affair which I expect will be the first of many.

The reason is simple enough: I want a proper sexual life and my husband does not. In fact, we have only had sex three times, and that was during the first fortnight of our marriage, on honeymoon. He is just not interested.

I have always assumed that my husband was asexual, but I am beginning to doubt this. I think he might be a gay. He seems to have homosexual leanings – I found some magazines full of pictures of men – and I wonder if it possible that these desires have developed since we got married.

 Is it normal for men to have feelings like this when they get older?

Yours sincerely,

J

Dear J – To answer to the final question first, I would say: "Yes, but only if they have a*lways* had feelings like this."

Your husband is gay, as clearly as you have a healthy heterosexual appetite. The affair doubtless brings you some pleasure, and you might think that nobody is getting hurt, but things cannot carry on like this indefinitely. You have to discuss these issues with your husband; the way things stand, there is no basis on which a long-term relationship between the two of you can possibly work.

In your longer letter, incidentally, you make no mention of children. Do you want to have a family? If not right now, what happens if you become 'broody' later? It doesn't sound to me as though your husband is going to welcome the prospect of fulfilling his part of the contract.

I would strongly advise that you discuss all these issues with your local Relate counsellor.

- 'Dr Mary', a Cull Valley general practitioner, donates her fee to a medical charity.

Stories they cannot print

DR VALERIE BERESFORD....

When I decided to cut down my hours at the surgery, I started looking round for a few new projects to interest me. It was Teddy who suggested that I might enjoy being an agony aunt for the Gazette, after a long-standing columnist had called it a day.

The editor was delighted to get someone who could bring medical expertise to the job, especially as I was filling half a page for £25. In quiet weeks, I've made up problems – with permission, of course – which are typical of the issues many people face, but that one was genuine.

Some stuff we get is astonishing. It's shocking in this day and age to get letters from newlyweds who don't know the first thing about sex, or teenage girls who think that you can't get pregnant the first time, or if they are standing up. On such occasions, I can provide booklets, information and sound advice. It makes the job worthwhile, knowing that you are helping someone.

More often, you have no idea how writers will respond to your help, and you are unlikely ever to find out. Will J realise that she must see a Relate counsellor, or will she ignore my advice and continue this affair?

"In your longer letter" was putting it mildly because J rambled on for several pages, telling me about the identity of her lover (the pro at the local golf club), about the stash of gay porn she found while rifling suspiciously through some of her husband's drawings of a proposed housing development (he is an architect), as well as a few other things that were nothing to the purpose, including her nice lifestyle, although, come to think of it, she probably does see that as a relevant factor in favour of staying put.

Teddy was intrigued by that problem, which we'd talked about in general terms over supper. I showed him my response to J – without revealing her identity, needless to say. In my personal letter to her, I was able to tell J a few home truths. "Your relationship with your husband sounds like a throwback to another era," I wrote. "In the 1950s and earlier, it was not uncommon for women to find themselves with gay husbands because they had not slept together before the nuptials; when pre-marital sex was frowned upon, the homosexual male in search of respectability could use a false gallantry to hide his preferences. Very occasionally, perhaps, there might be post-wedding relief on both sides as women who didn't like the idea of sex discovered that their husbands felt the same way."

But I would really like to have delivered it with both barrels, as I might have done if I'd been writing a similar column for a lads' magazine.

"Frankly, Love, straight sex for your chap would be as much fun as a wet and windy afternoon on the rugby pitch for the school's puniest boy. I'd just love to know what thoughts were going through his head on the few occasions that he brought things to a triumphant conclusion in the marital bed. One thing's for certain, they would not have involved you.

"He is not the first middle-aged husband to get caught with his underpants opened wide, and another bloke investigating the contents. Many men who are more gay than straight opt for the comforts and respectability of family life in their 20s. As they get older and their libido takes a dive, it's hardly surprising that they should turn to occasional, casual encounters featuring what they always liked best."

That would have been telling her.

My guess is that J will get a taste for casual affairs. When this fling fizzles out, she will probably move on to other unsuspecting and sexually biddable males, messing up numerous other lives in the process.

Julia's Journal

It's nice for a girl to have plenty of beaux, but you can have too much of a good thing!

Now that things with Teddy are moving forward, it's been Goodnight Vienna for Senior and Junior Admirers. I've always preferred swift actions and clean breaks and Junior Admirer didn't take it too badly, all things considered. I think he was pleased to have had a brief Season with Eros; it can't be easy chatting up girls in pubs and night clubs when you're hard of hearing. He's starting a proper job soon, so he'll be leaving the charity shop and I won't have to put up with much more of his love-sick puppy dog glances.

Senior Admirer was less phlegmatic, and no doubt miffed that he never even got to trouble the scorer. He's still, or so I've heard, got plenty of lead in his pencil, but I didn't put it to the test when the altogether more attractive, younger model became available to me in the shape of Teddy. A model, it should be said, not fazed by my reputation. However, my previous form is something that I need to distance myself from now. I don't want Teddy to think that this is just another fling, which is why I didn't allow him access to all areas on our first date. The disappointment on his face when I wouldn't go all the way was a sight for sore eyes, but sometimes you've got to play it mean to keep them keen.

Senior Admirer's appearance shortly before last orders in Cellar Vie was an unfortunate coincidence. It was crowded in there and I pretended not to have seen him, but I caught him giving the fabled Mrs T less than his full attention as he looked continually in our direction. I brushed a hand gently across

Teddy's face, to reinforce the message that this was well and truly end-of for Ken.

We finished our Peroni and headed off. I was a trifle put out to see that Teddy drove a Skoda Fabia, and only the entry model at that. "I don't earn a fortune, and I'm not very interested in cars," he said.

"Silly boy, there's more to life than money," I reassured him in the car park before we had our first, prolonged kiss.

It isn't going to be easy walking away from my new Mazda and the life of luxury in Green Pastures, though I'll never let Reggie go.

But sometimes you have to play the long game. With Teddy to take me on, I know that I can have my cake and ha'penny if I bide my time.

CULL VALLEY EVENING GAZETTE

Wednesday February 25 2009

A Walk on the mild side

Now then, young 'uns, a bit less bottle!

Our columnist and middle-aged fogey Kenneth 'Chuck' Thrower takes a light-hearted look at the way we live today, as he sticks up for the traditional way of enjoying a drink

As regular readers know, Thrower Towers is the venue for some fine dinner parties.

This is what happens every time we invite the cream of Hexroyd and Ainsley society to join us: we pick a selection of fine wines and knock them back, straight from the bottle.....

Well, obviously not.

But is the increasingly prevalent habit of drinking beer from the bottle any less preposterous?

Teenagers do it, as do many 20-somethings, and if I'm in a mellow frame of mind, I might just make allowances for youth. Is Chuck going a wee bit soft in late-middle age, I hear you saying? But old 'uns, (in this context surely anyone over the age of 30) should hang their heads in shame.

Do you think Oz Clarke and Jilly Goulden could tease out all those delicious poached aubergine and burnt cross-ply tyre tastes in their wine, if they were sticking a bottle neck down their throat? Of course not. As for Nigella Lawson, all credibility was lost here at TT, the evening we saw her on tele enjoying lunch with friends, and supping beer from the bottle.

Listen – or even listen up, Nige, if you prefer yoof-speak: "You are too old to get down with the kids. If you dislike beer, leave it alone. If you do like it, the only way you will be remotely able to appreciate its quality is from a glass."

And why, oh why, aren't bar staff trained to offer glasses to older customers? I'm (an admittedly youthful-looking) 59. I am not trying to look or behave as I did in 1968. I've lost count of the number of times I've asked for a malty Czech pilsner and been given nothing to pour it into.

Any customer who is happy with this state of affairs is sending out a simple message: "I am a complete Wally who is desperately trying to look cool. I think it's smart to behave as if my taste buds were surgically removed at birth."

What, you may ask yourselves, has brought forth this Chuckovian rant?

Well, I was in a wine bar recently and saw a man and a woman who should know better drinking a perfectly acceptable Italian lager straight from the bottle. (Mrs T had dragged me to the wine bar against my better judgment after a show, since you ask). Both these characters were in their 30s.

She was a curvaceous and pretty blonde, who shook her mane of hair in an affected manner. At the risk of upsetting the PC brigade, beer is not really a ladies' drink and you couldn't expect the lasses to know any better. But many of us blokes take our real ale very seriously. I can just about accept that he might drink an Italian lager in the absence of anything else. But no glass? Let's face it, he was simply trying to ingratiate himself with his lady friend.

So here's my proposal for the licensing trade, and it's a zero-tolerance affair: bar staff should be trained from the word go to insist that punters have a glass, so that the practice of drinking beer directly from the bottle withers on the vine, if you'll excuse my mixed alcoholic metaphor.

Incidentally, I shall be out and about in the pubs of Ainsley and Hexroyd with a copy of this newspaper during the next week or two. Anyone seen drinking from the bottle might find themselves subjected to the Chuck Thrower Challenge, and ordered to buy me a drink.

You have been warned! Cheers!

STORIES...KENNETH THROWER....

Nice Guy being played along by femme fatale blonde. Nice Guy believes he's being pushed out of frame because there's someone else. Nice Guy has curious encounter with jealous husband over question of personalised number plates. Nice Guy realises that his suspicions about love rival are correct. Nice Guy also finds out that love rival follows same trade. Nice Guy goes into work next day and sees office twat looking very pleased with himself. Nice Guy goes to wine bar and sees said office twat with femme fatale blonde...

Yes, there quaffing his birra Italiana senza una bicchiera stands the very man with whom the fancy-plates driver thought he was demanding that his wife should act discreetly.

Knowledge is power; as I ponder the form my revenge might take, conversation about the Cull Valley Opera's polished interpretation of Sweeney Todd is put on the back burner.

KCT is not a man who reacts warmly to defeat on the ladies' front; we now have a situation which must needs be exploited. It's no more Mr Nice Guy, Beresford.

Meanwhile, you never know your luck. The Chuck Thrower Challenge on drinking beer from the glass might prove a good opening gambit to chat up a few lasses.

The National Diary

From our files

How others see us....

First impressions of a foreign country can be hard to shift. French sports journalist Michel Malleret, of L'Equipe, loved Yorkshire and England, but was alarmed by the booze culture

I awoke to find my English pen pal lying in a pool of vomit.
"Was it the too good beer?" I said.
"Yes, it must have been," he groaned.

I had a great time staying with Teddy Beresford in West Yorkshire during the summer of 1992. His parents ("call us Phil and Val") were great, and Val's cooking dispelled many of my prejudices about English food. The Beresford family took me to York (the morning after the too good beer, unfortunately for Teddy), Whitby, the Dales and the North Yorks Moors; everyone talked to me constantly and engaged me in everything they did. My English came on a treat and that trip helped me make up my mind to study the language and literature at university.

The main thing that I couldn't get to grips with was the English booze culture. Many of Teddy's pals drank to excess, pouring horrible concoctions called alcopops down their throat until they were senseless. Phil and Val drank wine at home in much the same way that we did in France, and perhaps that's why Teddy was a bit more sensible than some of his peers.

But then came the night of alcoholic oblivion, which had its roots in a game of tennis. Like me, Teddy was keen on the game. We played a few times but I could see that his heart wasn't in it, and this was connected, I think, with events a week or so before I'd arrived in Ainsley. Teddy had lost the final of his local tennis club annual Under 18s' tournament. He was obsessed with the outcome of this event.

One night, in a local pub which turned a blind eye to under-age drinkers, he became very uncomfortable when someone called Tom walked in with a beautiful English rose of a girl called Rachel

Waterfall. As the beers went down the hatch (I lost count around the seven mark) the subject gradually switched from cricket, which I was getting to grips with, and football to this Rachel. The sight of Tom and Rachel sitting hand in hand at the bar was too much for Teddy. He kept saying something about how it should have been him, and talking about her too loudly.

Tom seemed a pleasant enough character. He came over and suggested, as politely as possible, that Teddy be quiet or leave. Teddy reacted like a spoilt child, at first sulking then putting his index finger to his mouth. "Everybody Do This," he said. Tom and Rachel gave him a pitiful look then left, which was the cue for Teddy to start whingeing again.

We staggered home with Teddy at closing time, and tried to get a few glasses of water down his throat. However, the damage was done. Teddy fell asleep almost instantly on hitting the bed and that's the way he stayed for a few hours before I was awoken by this dreadful retching sound.

I liked Teddy. He was amusing, polite and self-deprecating. Quite the young Englishman. He was a dreamy individual who'd go off into his own world. "That would make a story," he'd say if something unusual happened. I wasn't sure if he meant a newspaper story or a piece of fiction.

There was something ever so slightly lost and melancholic about him, as if he wasn't quite comfortable in his own skin or expected that every time he turned a street corner, there'd be a banana skin waiting to trip him up.

We kept in touch for a couple of years, but our correspondence eventually ran out of steam. I think about him from time to time, not least when I'm here to cover an Arsenal game, and I walk through the English streets at closing time, trying to dodge the raucous hen nights and street brawls.

I'm sure Teddy will have grown into a thoroughly civilised chap, perhaps with a young family. I bet he laughs at how upset he became over Rachel Waterfall.

J'espere, mon vieux camarade anglais, que tu and ta famille soient toujours heureux.

Advertisement Feature

(Draft copy, FAO Teddy Beresford)

Pets' corner

Many of us have fond memories of an especially treasured pet when we were children.

For me, it was a budgerigar with a wonderful personality. I could get Charlie out of his cage and he'd fly round the room before landing on my head. Charlie was happy to sit in the goods van of my toy train while it did a couple of circuits of the living room. Toot toot! Happy days.

Sad to report, Charlie's sociability was his undoing. One day, he stood on the carpet and watched as I did a handstand. I lost my balance, fell on Charlie and he flew no more.

"Oh, Stanley Winston Cartwright, what have you done?" said my mother, who only addressed me with my full Sunday name when she was very upset.

But it's better to have loved and lost. I loved Charlie and I loved caring for him. Here in the Cull Valley, small pets such as budgies, hamsters and guinea pigs are all available from Pet World in Market Street, Ainsley. Shop owner Bobby Owen says that it's a great idea to start youngsters off with little creatures before they move on to owning and looking after those outrageously demanding monsters of the pet world, cats and dogs. Bobby can offer plenty of tips on pet ownership, too.

He adds: "Having pets can help children to come to terms with mortality. The death of a hamster or a gerbil can be quite upsetting for a young person, but it can be part of their growing understanding of life's natural cycle."

Dogs need to behave properly and that's where experts such as Gilly Deer of Hexroyd come in. Gilly says that it's best to get dogs trained when they are still puppies although, contrary to popular belief, you *can* teach an old dog new tricks.

"It just takes a bit longer," argues Gilly, whose 'clients' range from dachshunds to German shepherds.

Unsurprisingly, Gilly reports that, among older dogs, the worst-behaved animals tend to be the smelliest. "The people who've let things go, and let their dogs get away with things are often the ones who can't be bothered to give Fido an occasional scrub."

Pigs, of course, are renowned as exceptionally smelly animals, and not meant to be kept as pets, although that has not, in recent years, stopped a few people keeping the Vietnamese pot-bellied variety in their back yard.

It's a little known fact that pigs, perhaps the most delightful of all God's creatures, are not naturally smelly. Like gas, the smell is added later. But rather than being a health and safety issue, the aim is to discourage excessive numbers of people from turning to pig farming and thereby creating an imbalance in the agricultural economy.

This is not news, of course, to fans of Albeit Albert, the Cull Valley's celebrated 1970s' band, whose rock anthem *Pig Farmers*, from their concept album, *All Creatures Great and Small*, celebrates man's closest relative in the farmyard. Their big song closes with the words: 'Porkers, though pongers, are absolute charmers, no smell and we'd all want to be pig farmers'.

From: Edward.beresford@univalleypapers.co.uk
Date: 5 March, 2009 16:26
To: Stanley.cartwright@univalleypapers.co.uk
Subj: No band here, you lying bastard

I have followed the local rock scene for more than 20 years. Further back, my mother and father saw the only performances by Eric Clapton, Steve Winwood and Van Morrison in the Cull Valley. They also witnessed the rise of our area's biggest band, Triangular Hour. None of us has ever, ever heard of anyone called Albeit Albert. (Advertisement feature, Pets' Corner) What's going on?

Perhaps Mr Stanley Winston Cartwright claims that Elvis has been here too!

Yrs, Teddy

From: Edward.beresford@univalleypapers.co.uk
Date: 5 March, 2009 15:00
To: Stanley.cartwright@univalleypapers.co.uk
Subj: Smell? They're as high as fucking kites!

I have been a pig farmer for many, many years. I aver with the view of the columnist (Advertisement feature, Pets' corner) when he says that they are right charming creatures. Indeed, they have been grand companions for me throughout my working life. But I'll tell him this, for nowt. They don't arrive in the world smelling fresh, and neither does it get any better. A pig stinks from day one and she don't need no artificial additives to make thee know it. Perhaps your writer should dig out a cracking film called *Waking Ned*. Happen it'll help him to understand the problems porkers can create in the romantic affairs of us custodians.

Yrs, Teddy

STORIES....STAN CARTWRIGHT....

Pets' corner. Has the career of Stanley Cartwright finally bottomed out?

As I said, suggesting to Mark McClair that he should do his own dirty work was not clever. When I got home, early 2002 it would have been, I decided to come clean with Suzanne. I'd grumbled about Reuben Parfitt's stupidity often enough. Suddenly, though, I'd gone over the top in my support for him. Suzanne flew right off the handle and I knew why.

"We might as well sign into the workhouse now," she said.

But Mark McClair kept his powder dry for a few weeks, and I began to wonder if I'd got away with it. Until, that is, the day we all gathered to pay our tributes to Reuben.

McClair ran his hand across his smooth head, adjusted his spectacles and coughed delicately to call for silence. Reuben waited nervously, licking his lips and exercising his mouth, as if to ensure that, when called on, he would still have the power of speech.

"We're here to say goodbye to Reuben Parfitt," McClair said when he was satisfied that everyone in the newsroom had settled down. "Now, where to begin the story of a man who has become a part of the furniture at the Gazette and who I like to think of as a personal friend?"

Reuben looked awestruck by this expression of kinship, like a squaddie invited to share a pint with a field marshal.

"In 1969," said McClair, sounding like Alan Partridge, "there was...Something in the Air. That was the number one smash hit single for Thunderclap Newman, but the...Something in the Air....that I'm referring to was the arrival of Reuben Parfitt in the Cull Valley.

"It's a little known fact that newspapers weren't Reuben Parfitt's first calling. He started as a butcher, a trade which he assures me has nothing in common with journalism."

Polite laughter and more astonishment from Reuben, who couldn't recall the exchange.

"Since coming with Dorothy from Leicestershire there are few editorial jobs you haven't done and you've tackled them all, if I may say so Reuben – reporter, sub editor, features writer, even bowls correspondent – in a manner which has been exemplary.

"In fact I think I am right in saying your passion for bowls is such that, immediately after you arrived here from the Leicester County Argus and the removal men had done their work, you went off to introduce yourself to the chaps playing at the local park, neglecting to pass this information on to Dorothy."

There was belated laughter as Mark McClair smiled thinly over this insubstantial anecdote.

"I'll bet Reuben never did that again," Jim Stafford whispered to me.

"Which, of course, was in 1969, the year of Thunderclap Newman...," continued McClair, looking pleased with himself over the beautifully-crafted and circular nature of his speech.

He adjusted his glasses and looked over them into the assembled crowd, to indicate that a serious bit was coming up.

"It's always sad to see one of the 'old guard' going but it's also exciting to grasp new opportunities. The next few months will see substantial changes on the editorial floor and I'm sure that you will all rise to the challenges ahead. Youth will, where appropriate, be given its head and no one will be allowed to continue to inhabit comfort zones they have created for themselves and their cronies. This place is no respecter of reputations which are past their sell-by date."

"That's telling us," I said to Stafford, who'd also been known to stand up to McClair.

Our leader glanced at his watch and wound up his speech. His words were highly acclaimed; no one wanted to stop clapping first.

Reuben made a deferential speech, thanked United and Valley Newspapers for the generous redundancy package, thanked his friends and colleagues for the parting gifts and framed mock-up front page featuring him as the big story, and concluded: "I suppose I could always go back to my old trade," which, for some reason, brought the house down.

Jim Stafford, who'd been courted by a couple of nationals during his days covering Park Avenue, took the editor's hint. Before he could crash into the singularity at the centre of McClair's universe, he went off to do his sports work on a paper somewhere in the Midlands. With my kids getting along well at school, I decided to stay put. Naturally, the axe did fall. I was shipped out to be a district reporter, covering a remote patch of the valley from a small office above a newsagent's.

Four years later, as part of a United and Valley Newspapers rationalisation, the office was closed.

"But we might be able to find something for you back at head office, Stan," said McClair.

CULL VALLEY EVENING GAZETTE

Classifieds

Saturday February 16 1980

SECOND-HAND MOTORS

1966 Ford Anglia (red), good runner, needs some attention, would suit enthusiast, £150 ono.

Julia's Journal

Ravello on the Amalfi coast is a gorgeous little town, and the waiters are to die for! Anthony certainly thinks so! In different circumstances, I'd be severely tempted myself. I wouldn't blame him for dipping a toe in the water, as long as he's not too in-your-face about it. But Tony's far too uptight for anything like that.

I'm settling for plenty of Pinot Grigio and early nights so I can snuggle down, pleasantly sozzled, and think about Teddy; imagine him making love to me in our snug Barrowclough Mill apartment.

Whenever that might be. Because some long-term commitment wouldn't be a bad thing.

There are one or two practical issues to confront first. I've not exactly gone down a treat with Teddy's parents. I've only met them twice and I feel that I'm being scrutinised very closely, as if I'm some kind of case study. His mum looks at me as if I'm verging on the barking. It's possible (though unlikely) that she remembers the letter I wrote to her in her capacity as the Gazette's agony aunt, in which case Teddy's protestations that we are just good friends would not ring true. I am trying to get Teddy to come straight about our relationship. "It's too early days," he says. "Why don't you just let me stay the night without telling them and spell it out that way, she doesn't buy this good friends business," I say. "Mum and Dad wouldn't approve, you're a married woman," he says. I was on the verge of saying: "But you're my husband, spiritually." I bit my tongue; too much, too soon, Lady.

Venues for nookie are causing some headaches, too. I'm fairly sure that Anthony found some evidence of our activities at Green Pastures the other week. He's not said anything so far, but I'll have to watch my step. We've stayed over at Rory and Ruth's twice, but I can tell that there's been some disagreement between Paddy and Miss Prissy Golden Girl Nolan about the rights and wrongs of that one. In any case, they're not the greatest of hosts, as they showed all too clearly by their grumpy reaction to our lie-in the other day. We might be better off chez Nolan when they're on holiday and Teddy's going in to water the plants and pick up the post.

Anyway, mid-term report on E Beresford:

1) In bed: enthusiasm compensates for lack of technique but making steady progress.

2) Out of bed: Must try harder, and show that he really is in it for the duration.

𝔗𝔥𝔢 𝔑𝔞𝔱𝔦𝔬𝔫𝔞𝔩 𝔇𝔦𝔞𝔯𝔶

May 2009

Quidnunc

Keep tabs on the stars without having to read the Tabs

The Red Tops report that earlier this year Julia Yates dumped "not one but two guys" who have escorted her in recent months. The reason: she has finally found love.

The demise of 25-year-old Andy Dougan, personable but penniless, had been predicted by insiders at Ainsley Battling Cancer. But the disappearance from the picture of veteran Hexroyd Lothario Kenneth 'Chuck' Thrower took everyone by surprise.

However, that is nothing to the shock felt by her new love, Teddy Beresford. He had assumed that Julia would have moved on by now after two or three heady months of carefree sex. It hasn't worked out that way: Julia made it clear, before heading off for a well-earned break in Ravello, that she now wants some commitment from Teddy. She has been applying pressure on him to put down a deposit on one of the former Barrowclough Mill apartments which are now selling for 15 per cent less than their 2008 price.

According to the *Daily Reflector*, one insider at the *Cull Valley Evening Gazette* says: "Julia is now seriously into Teddy Beresford, and all previous dalliances are ancient history. I know that she does fall in love very easily, but she's a different woman now – determined to achieve a total lifestyle overhaul which will see Teddy installed permanently as the only man in her life."

Meanwhile – so the *Daily Messenger* reports – Julia might be getting broody. The *Messenger*'s celebrities editor is predicting that Julia will soon start pushing for the patter of tiny feet.

A couple close to Beresford have declined to talk to the *Messenger* about their friend, so it is difficult to determine how the provincial journalist would react to such a radical development. Rumour has it that he's enjoying his "week off" while Julia and Anthony get some spring sunshine in Italy.

Beresford is probably bracing himself for a renewed assault on his independence when Julia flies home. He will have to be tough; he's never had to deal with such a formidable partner. Just how he will go about letting her down gently can only be a matter of uninformed speculation.

Meanwhile, he also fears that he might have incurred the wrath of *Gazette* deputy editor Kenneth 'Chuck' Thrower. It took a while for Thrower to reconcile himself to Julia's negative vibes and there could yet be a confrontation between him and Teddy. At the ferociously hierarchical *Gazette*, Chuck is an officer and Teddy is one of the men. If Thrower is still feeling humiliated and the two stags lock horns, Beresford, a former wannabe tennis star, could be in trouble.

CULL VALLEY EVENING GAZETTE

Wednesday May 6 2009

A love that binds two hearts together

You won't hear Rory and Ruth Nolan saying that absence makes the heart grow fonder. Hazel Moses continues her weekly examination of family business partnerships by focusing on two book-binders who work together in perfect harmony

Draw up a list of the qualities that make for an ideal husband and it's a safe bet that Rory Nolan would tick most of the boxes.

The softly-spoken Irishman can turn his hand to any job around the house, he prefers a night at the cinema or theatre to an evening in the pub with his mates, and – you'll just love this bit, girls – he has absolutely no interest in sport.

"Tussles with the remote have never been a feature of our domestic life," laughs his wife, Ruth. "Rory would much rather watch *Foyle's War* or a repeat of *Morse*, than *Match of the Day* and *Channel 4 Racing*."

The circumstances that led to Rory becoming a book-binder are somewhat unusual; however, he tells me, the fact that Ruth ended up working with him in the trade is doubly astonishing.

Why should book-binding be a male preserve, I'm wondering before a penetrating look from Rory's blue eyes tell me that I'm on the wrong lines.

"What I'm saying, Hazel, is that I only discovered my skills as a matter of chance. I'd never considered book-binding as a career. And Ruth only discovered her talents because I'd discovered mine."

It all started when Rory was in his first year as a science teacher at a school in Torquay, and his landlord was a bookseller.

Rory explains: "He asked me if I knew anything about binding. I got a library book and started to teach myself, practising on my landlord's stock. He even knocked a bit off the rent at one point in part payment for my efforts. He said that I seemed to have a knack, and it was only then that I decided to take it further by going to college in London, to immerse myself thoroughly in the skills of the trade.

"In many ways, it was the answer to my prayers. Unlike Ruth, it was very quickly becoming clear that I wasn't going to be able to hack it in the classroom."

Ruth's teaching work kept them both afloat financially while Rory completed his training. They moved to Yorkshire and gradually – and mainly by word of mouth – acquired a growing number of clients.

Two significant 'breaks' made all the difference. First, they found the perfect spot for Rory's job, above a china shop in one of Hexroyd's oldest buildings. It's a lovely use of space. The workshop is divided by an area in the middle with a pair of big squashy sofas. The medieval room has uneven oak floors and huge beams supporting the exposed roof trusses. It's painted white and three high windows on one side let in all the light they need. Secondly, a couple of years after moving here, Rory got himself the sort of contract that must be the book binding equivalent of being taken on by one of the major supermarket chains.

"We got Piper House," he says, simply.

You feel that, several years on, he is still tempted to punch the air as if in post-goal triumph. As *Gazette* readers will recall, our area's most famous stately home was one of the local winners when National Lottery funding came on stream. Lord Brigg got the money to restore the Piper House library and Rory got the book-binding contract. It gave Rory two years' guaranteed work and Lord Brigg couldn't speak highly enough of him, which in turn opened a few more doors.

This was the point at which Ruth was able to join the business. Things were going so well that they no longer needed her full-time teaching income. She'd been helping out occasionally and discovered that, like Rory, she had a natural aptitude.

Rory says: "You need good hands, to be of a practical bent, but when you're dealing with old books you've got to be sympathetic to the style of the original. You can't treat every book as if it's the same. Ruth picked it all up very quickly, and I'd say that she's probably now at least as good if not better at some aspects of the job than I am."

But doesn't working together bring its own set of problems? I mean, being together all the time. I love my hubby Jim dearly but we both need a bit of space.

"Not at all, Hazel," says Ruth. "We don't argue, we're very comfortable together. We tend to sort out any grumbles in the next

155

sentence, if you know what I mean. In any case, I still get out occasionally for a bit of teaching supply work. But I love the paraphernalia of book-binding – the morocco, pigskin, leather, glue, dyes, period endpapers."

At work and play, Rory and Ruth continue to sing from the same hymn sheet!

The National Diary

May 2009

How much do I earn?

Wages and salaries. Some of us are coy about our pay packet, others want to sing it from the roof tops. This week we turn our focus to some of the lowest-paid professional people in the country, provincial journalists. Teddy Beresford, of the Cull Valley Gazette, comes clean.

I am a 34-year-old sub-editor on an evening newspaper in Yorkshire, and I earn about £23,000 a year. Some of my colleagues are worse off.

I came back to my home patch 12 years ago with a university degree and a postgraduate qualification in journalism. I was a news reporter and also worked on the features desk for a while before joining the 'subs', albeit not entirely of my own volition, a few years ago.

My colleagues and I have occasionally found ourselves in the position, so galling to provincial journalists, of writing articles which make reference to pay in other trades and professions – almost invariably more than we pick up ourselves.

As a single chap living with my parents I've never had any difficulty in making ends meet. I wouldn't, however, want to be a family man on that kind of pay, unless I had a wife who was happy to go straight back to work after giving birth to our children.

There are great opportunities in journalism, but you've got to be very focused on your career if you really want to get on, whether it's in broadcasting, public relations, national newspapers or freelancing. I've not done that. But I knew the score when I entered the trade, and I've only got myself to blame for the position in which I find myself now. So I'm not here to whinge, not least because my actual job is okay. But a bit more money would be nice and the issue I'm concerned about *is* related indirectly to my earnings.

I'm here to talk about a curious development in my life. I am having an affair with a beautiful woman. Far from being (my original assumption) a casual fling, she has in the last two months started, almost imperceptibly at first but of late ever more overtly, to take it very seriously; it is increasingly evident that she wants me to buy a flat so that she can leave her seriously affluent husband and we can move in together.

At first, I found it hard to believe that she could possibly think that way. Julia is very mercenary and likes her lifestyle, even if her marriage is going nowhere. As for me, I'm not a lawyer, doctor, accountant or businessman. What does she think that I can offer her?

I sussed it finally: I had two factors running in my favour and one was being the only child of affluent parents. It must have occurred to Julia that they couldn't be expected to go on for ever. And even if they both survived into their 80s, there would presumably in the meantime be plenty of support for their only son, daughter-in-law and any young offspring.

On Julia's first visit to my parents' house, she said: "Isn't it large?" "Therefore worth a few bob," she might as well have added. And for someone with no previous interest in art, she was remarkably enthusiastic about Mum and Dad's collection, including an Atkinson Grimshaw and some Jacob Kramer lithographs.

The other factor which might have made me a potentially attractive long-term partner in Julia's eyes was good genes. Dad was a rugby scrum-half and paediatrician and Mum, a county tennis player, had been a GP.

Before I worked all this out for myself, I'd been like the cat that'd got the cream with Julia, and we probably irritated a few people in that early phase when we couldn't leave one another alone. I found myself getting involved far too deeply. My 'see the carpet' safety mechanism, which usually prevents me from living too dangerously, or losing sight of life's realities, kicked in too late.

Julia and I have had a few dodgy moments. There was the time my friend Ruth observed, apropos of nothing and exaggerating no doubt, that the Barrowclough Mill apartments had dropped in price by almost a third. "I keep on telling you that you want to get in now," said Julia. "They've probably not yet bottomed out, best to sit tight a while," I said.

I then spotted Rory and Ruth doing one of their synchronised waving of the eyebrows. They knew that *I* knew bugger all about property, and whether apartment prices were likely to go up or down. What I should have been saying, put more delicately, was: "I'm not moving from Mum and Dad's, or getting any more serious, Love. This is as good as it gets, so take it or leave it."

Just when I will pick up the courage to say that is anybody's guess, though I might allow myself a few more weeks of fun. I don't suppose this quality of sex is likely to be on offer to me anywhere else in the foreseeable future, if ever.

CULL VALLEY EVENING GAZETTE

Monday June 8 2009

Botched routine floors morris dancer

New manoeuvre was not strictly traditional
By Gavin Layton

The gentle and traditional English pastime of morris dancing has never had a reputation for being a tough contact sport.

But all that changed on Carnival Day when a new rugby-inspired routine dreamed up by the Cull Valley Shakers went horribly wrong outside the Anglers Arms in Lower Ainsley.

As Anthony Yates went to the left in the elaborate 'Rugby Shuffle' manoeuvre, co-dancer Joshua Mulhearn elected to make a move into the same space. In the resulting collision, Mr Yates broke his ankle.

It brought an abrupt end to the Shakers' plans to dance at six venues throughout Ainsley and Hexroyd as part of the Cull Valley Carnival. Instead, Mr Yates, a local architect and deputy chairman of Mid-Pennine Chamber of Commerce, was rushed to hospital and the other members of the Shakers retired for an early pint.

Mr Mulhearn said: "The idea behind the 'Rugby Shuffle' was that at a certain point in the dance each man in the group has to lower his left shoulder as he approaches his co-dancer. But like a rugby winger selling a dummy, he's actually going to move in the other direction.

"Of course, the 'wrong' direction is the one his 'opponent' should take so that the dummy has been sold, avoiding contact in the process. But for some reason, mea culpa, I got my lefts and rights mixed up and just barged into Tony. It was most unfortunate, a bit of a misunderstanding, during a routine that wasn't strictly morris dancing but which would have looked terrific if it had come off. In normal circumstances, Tony would simply have got up, a wee bit red-faced, and we'd all have carried on. He just happened to fall awkwardly.

"We might have done better if we'd rehearsed it properly. One or two members of the team felt there was an element of showboating, and the rugby league fans among the lads felt that it should have been called the Union Shuffle, because it was such a cock-up!

"But you've got to push the envelope occasionally to keep the art alive for future generations. Morris dancing mustn't turn into a fossilised relic of Merrie England."

Mr Yates, who was X-rayed, in plaster and home by early evening, exchanged a few angry words with Mr Mulhearn following the incident, but was philosophical when the *Gazette* spoke to him later.

"It's just one of those things," he said. "It'll be frustrating to have to work from home for the next few weeks, but I'll manage. I hope to be out and about, and joining the Shakers again before the summer is over."

STORIES....GAVIN LAYTON....

As Stan Cartwright said to me, that's never going happen very often: unless you're a sports reporter there won't be many of those rare and happy occasions when you actually witness the decisive moment.

I was chuffed that I hadn't been saddled with the job of covering Cull Valley Carnival. I was minding my own business over a quiet lunchtime pint of Golden Accelerator in the Anglers Arms when the Morris dancers turned up with their whoops, yelps, fiddles and accordions. Even those bloody bells piss you off once you've got them in your head, like a dripping tap when you're trying to get some zeds.

I decided to have another pint elsewhere, and came out of the pub to see all the Shakers in a huddle, examining a stricken figure.

This Mulhearn guy was saying to Anthony Yates: "Get up you Big Jessie, even Didier Drogba wouldn't have the nerve to go down on such a slight contact."

Yates replied: "I think I've broken something you fucking eejit."

It was just an accident and Yates was OK about it when I phoned him at home the following morning, although I thought it was a trifle po-faced not to let us take a picture of him with his ankle in plaster, smiling as he accepted a kiss and cheering, consolation cuppa from his lovely wife, Julia. But we'd got a decent file picture of him leading the Shakers in one of their more successful routines.

Chuck Thrower thought the whole thing was hilarious and spent the morning coming out with feeble quips about up and unders. The sycophants on the subs' desk joined in, with the exception of Teddy Beresford.

When I wandered over to Teddy, expecting a compliment about my off-the-diary story, all he could say was: "For fuck's sake, why have you spelt Merry with an 'ie'."

"It looks better that way, you know, in the context of the story."

"That's going to be your policy on spelling from now on, is it? Whether words look nice or not, in the context of the story?" He waved his head theatrically as he said the last bit in a silly voice, to emphasise how precious I was being.

"Christ, what's eating you today?" I said, walking away. "Don't take your romantic problems out on me."

"You changed your mind then?" I asked later at the drinks machine, when the paper had been printed.

"Come again, Gav."

"About Merry and Merrie."

"Oh, yeah, I decided you were right on reflection, sorry about that," he said absent-mindedly.

As I walked back to my desk, Chuck Thrower was playing with his braces, and doing a daft northern accent.

"Reet, lads, let's dance the Up and Under."

Even the other subs were no longer amused. But looking again at Teddy, I wondered if he was out of sorts because my story reminded him about his problems with Julia. Anthony Yates's permanent presence in Green Pastures for the next few weeks will cramp the lovers' style. If that encourages Teddy to finally ditch Julia, it would be no bad thing.

The National Diary

June 2009

Thirteen reasons to oppose the Union

More than 100 years after the historic split, Henry Hawley discovers that the two worlds of morris dancing are as divided as ever

As a working-class lad, it was only right and proper that my father should introduce me to the world of morris dancing league before I went to grammar school.

Dad and I went to watch the Cull Valley Shakers outside the Rose and Crown in Hexroyd and it was the most exciting afternoon of my life. The Shakers were absolutely on the top of their game and the combination of sights, sounds and smells – swords and handkerchiefs, sticks and bells, stale beer and Capstan full-strength cigarettes – created a multi-sensory delight that will stay with me for ever.

It's a source of great pride for all of us in the Cull Valley that the Shakers were one of the founding members of the Morris Dancing League. Along with 20 other clubs, they met at the George Hotel in Huddersfield in 1895, to break away from the Union and dance semi-professionally.

Dad's timing, taking me to the Rose and Crown as a ten-year-old, was impeccable. I was old enough to appreciate what I was seeing, but too young to entirely understand and therefore feel intimidated by the raw and unforgiving world of the professional morris dancer, in which one wrong manoeuvre can lead to broken limbs and shattered careers. First impressions count for so much and Dad breathed a sigh of relief when the Shakers delivered the goods that afternoon, and he knew he'd got a convert on his hands. Because, catastrophically, I was heading for West Pennine Grammar, a bastion of the detested morris dancing union. I'll never forget Dad's words to me before I set off for my first day at the big boys' school: "Always flout the Union dancing rules, and never forget your working-class roots."

I haven't let him down, and a recent story in the *Cull Valley Gazette* reminded me that the sporting rectitude of at least some of the Shakers remains as unimpeachable as ever. These anti-Union members are unswerving in their loyalty to the 13-a-side dance game and they've maintained their integrity in a world that is changing at a sometimes bewildering pace. It is curiously reassuring to know that the worlds of morris dancing league and morris dancing union remain poles apart.

Of course, the historical reason behind the split has gone. There's professionalism in both codes now and dancers are free to move from one to the other without fear of censure. The days of southerners having trials with League teams, and dancing as A N Other have long gone.

But attempts to form sides combining the best of both codes, to create a sport that could ultimately challenge the international supremacy of ballroom dancing, are surely doomed to failure. Both sides remain intransigent. Who can forget the late and legendary BBC commentator Tom McAdam, so upset when the star member of his local side opted to go League, that he said: "He's doing his morris dancing elsewhere." He couldn't even bring himself to say the words morris dancing league.

As for me, I've lived in Twickenham for a few years now, right in the heart of morris dancing union country. I rarely get a chance to see the League boys in action. But I remain as true to my roots as ever, and as prejudiced against Union as Tom McAdam ever was towards us Leaguers.

When I read about The Cull Valley Shakers, and the Rugby Shuffle, I was transported as if it were yesterday back to the Rose and Crown circa 1985, to the smell of Dad's baccy and the dampness of our pet whippet Rosie's nose, as she poked inside my trouser pocket to sniff the dead stag beetle and half-sucked gobstopper I'd put there for safe keeping.

Say it out loud, I'm Morris Dancing League and I'm Proud.

CULL VALLEY EVENING GAZETTE

Classifieds
Saturday August 19 1995

CLASSIC CARS

Immaculate, restored sunburst red 1966 Ford Anglia. Reluctant seller going abroad. £1,500 ono.

The National Diary

June 2009

Ask Jenny

If it has to be said, agony aunt Jenny Dudley won't pull her punches

'Am I being blackmailed by my boss?'

Dear Jenny – Remember me? I told you that I might embark on an affair with a married woman, and that I would let you know how matters progressed. Well, I regret to have to tell you that I did succumb to temptation. I have been very worried about how I am going to handle the break with her, and I was very depressed about it at work the other day.

I thought we'd been discreet, but my boss has found out about the affair. It was just sheer bad luck – he saw us together in the sort of wine bar I wouldn't have expected him to frequent. I rather hoped against hope that nothing more would be said. But I know him too well. After a couple of days of eyeing me up like a bird of prey waiting for the right moment, he called me into his office.

"Teddy," he said, "We're having a few problems with the graveyard shift. Perhaps you could help us out."

I'm a sub-editor on the local evening paper. The graveyard shift is from 4pm to around midnight. No one likes to do it but we all have to take our turn. I pointed out to Kenneth that, as a single man without family commitments, I already do more than my fair share. Now I was being asked to do three a week, because a couple of his cronies didn't fancy it.

"I realise that this might eat into your colourful private life," he said. He might as well have added: "It would be a pity if anyone were to find out."

He's got me over a barrel. I said I'd do it for the next few weeks, while one or two staff are on holiday, then we could discuss it again.

I feel already as if I've just rolled over without a fight and right now I'm so down about it that it's having an effect on my work and my relationships with colleagues. I was unnecessarily sharp with a reporter the other day over something really trivial.

My boss, Kenneth, he's the deputy editor by the way, is a toad. He's also a sexist red-neck as anyone with half a brain reading *Take a Walk on the Mild Side*, his exasperating (though by no means incompetent, he does hit the mark occasionally) and faux-chummy column would agree. To that list you might as well add hypocrite, because he tried unsuccessfully to cop off with the very same woman I'm seeing now. And you can bet your bottom dollar that, given half the chance, he would throw over his beloved 'Mrs T' for at least three women in the editorial and advertising departments.

In view of my early capitulation to his demands at work, I'm not sure what my next step should be, Jenny. What do you advise?

Yrs Teddy

Dear Teddy – What's the frequency of Kenneths? I've certainly come across a few of them in my time. My first somewhat flippant observation is that I'm surprised he didn't have something more unpleasant up his sleeve.

Yes, as you realise, you *were* wrong to capitulate so easily. The chances are that Kenneth will now see you as fair game when he wants a few 'favours'. If I were you, I would keep my head down, carry out those shifts as promised and then resolutely refuse to be compromised in future.

It's a shade melodramatic to start suggesting that you go into the next meeting with a tape recorder hidden on your person. I'm far from convinced that he would carry out his threats, or refer to them directly. I also suspect that quite a few people already know about the affair, beyond the odd person you've told, such as Gavin Layton. Word gradually seeps out with these things, you know.

Again, at the risk of being flippant, would your extra-marital affair be so frowned on? I've worked in some places where affairs appeared to be almost de rigueur.

Don't get me wrong, I'm not condoning adultery, and I would urge you to resolve things with this woman as soon as possible, ideally by ending the affair altogether.

That would certainly be the end of any hold this rebarbative man has on you. You seem to suggest you want out of the relationship. Split with this woman now and you could have Kenneth off your back as well, killing two birds with one stone.

Yrs Jenny

CULL VALLEY EVENING GAZETTE

Wednesday June 24 2009

Dr Mary's Surgery

Our no-holds-barred medical adviser and agony aunt examines your problems

Dear Dr Mary – My husband is behaving very strangely. Before he goes out "with the lads" as he puts it, he has a shower, changes into his best clothes and sprinkles on the after shave. In all his years of meeting mates at the pub he has never done this. In fact, I used to pull him up on occasion for going out looking a right old mess.

When we met my husband's best friend recently, he had no recollection that they'd been in the pub together the evening before. Then, as if to make up for this brief loss of memory, he kept saying: "As I was only observing in the local last night."

Do you think my husband is having an affair?

Yrs sincerely,

N

Dear N – Yes, I think he is. There would appear to be no other explanation. The question you should really be asking is what you intend to do about. Does it worry you unduly? Has he strayed before? Is your relationship an apparently happy one? Unless I know the answer to some of these questions, it's hard to offer advice. But I would suggest that you need to tell him that it's obvious what is going on. As things stand, your husband is walking all over you and making you look like a bit of a ninny.

> 'Dr Mary', a Cull Valley general practitioner, donates her fee to a medical charity.

STORIES...DR VALERIE BERESFORD....

I was tempted to answer N with one word: 'Yes'. But the Gazette readers do expect a little more.

In my full, private response to N, who told me she worked in a local supermarket, I expressed astonishment about her husband's transparency, but also explained more gently that the clues were there.

I'm sure that Philip would play his cards a little closer to his chest than N's chap, but he has a similar lack of guile. It's one of things that first attracted me to him; I'd certainly know if he was playing away. Teddy is more subtle, but only marginally so. I know he's lying when he says that his friendship with the dreadful Yates girl is purely platonic. She isn't remotely his type, other than at a purely physical level.

As for Julia, she isn't easy to read; if my memory serves, she was one of the first people I ever dealt with on the problem page about three years ago. So, I know she likes sex and isn't getting any at home. But I get the feeling there's more to it than that. Is she seeking a permanent change of partner, and is Teddy the target?

I've only met her three times; the first was an embarrassing chance encounter in a local café. But it's abundantly clear that she lacks empathy and is unable to identify with the feelings of other people.

She's got some unsightly scars on her left arm, which Teddy told me were the result of a savage attack by a dog when she was a little girl. I suspect that it's really self-harm, especially as she's right-handed and the scars are left arm only.

I expressed sympathy over her husband's morris dancing accident, just about managing to keep a straight face. She reacted as if she were a martyr, waiting on him hand and foot. She sounded like Mother Teresa. So much for "in sickness and in health". As for her charity shop work, she talked as if everything would fall apart if she weren't there.

I think that Julia's got some kind of Narcissistic Personality Disorder: lack of perspective, failure to identify with the feelings of anyone else, and preoccupation with her own difficult circumstances.

She doesn't sound to me like a very self-sufficient sort of person. Narcissists are often poor at coping alone, while having a high opinion of themselves in all sorts of arenas. Like the bedroom. One reason I remember Julia's letter to me (this didn't make it to the highly-edited version in the Gazette) was because she said: "I am really good at sex." Narcissistic females are often impressive and inventive sexual athletes because they like to take control.

Philip and I are especially alarmed by this relationship because Edward tried to kill himself last year. We worry about him now we realise what a vulnerable young man he is.

I can hardly expect to hear that Teddy has taken the sensible step of ending the affair with Julia, as he's never admitted to it in the first place. But to be told that he had stopped seeing her, that they were no longer friends, would be music to my ears. Why did Edward have to go for her, when there are so many attractive and unattached girls around?

It's another one-word answer. Sex.

CULL VALLEY EVENING GAZETTE

Thursday October 9, 2008

'My debt to the Cull Valley'

Jeannie Derby meets Tom Waterfall, the former Hexroyd boy who has won universal praise for *Holiday Stories,* his first film to receive a major theatrical release.

Tom Waterfall's most prized possession is his late father's scrapbook.

You can see immediately why it means so much to Tom, the acclaimed director and co-writer of a new British feature. The well-thumbed old volume, like the film, is called *Holiday Stories.*

In fact, it doesn't look at first glance like a scrapbook at all. You would appear to have in your hands a volume of short and light-hearted tales – the front cover carries a picture of a 1950s' bathing belle holding a beach ball.

Tom, who is visiting Hexroyd for a special charity screening, says: "This book is important because it told you so much about my dad and was the inspiration behind my film, *Holiday Stories.*"

Open it and you will see the words: "Things that I have found interesting by Clifford Hogg."

Tom explains: "My paternal grandfather was a printer, and he brought this book home from work when my father was about 10 or 11, so he could use it as a scrapbook. It was a cast-off because the first print run had gone wrong and most of the inside pages were blank. So Dad, who later worked on and off in the printing trade himself, used it for a collection of cuttings from newspapers, which showed the breadth and changing nature of his interests, from sport and film stars to music and science as he got into his teens.

"He was not an educated man, but he loved reading and always encouraged me to believe that I could go far if I worked hard."

Tragically, as we see in the feature film, Clifford Hogg died when Tom was very young but he took his father's words to heart, eventually going from Hexroyd Grammar School to Cambridge University, where he read history.

Although Tom took an interest in student journalism, he turned to the advertising world after graduating and became a copywriter with a top London agency. This led to the opportunity to write and direct television adverts, as Alan Parker and Ridley Scott had done in the 1960s. Eventually, his brilliant visual style came to the attention of leading producer Derek Plimstock, and with it the chance to direct a short film based on H G Wells' story *The Door in the Wall*. A BAFTA nomination gave him the opportunity to spread his wings with a bigger project – *Holiday Stories* which he directed and co-wrote with novelist Helena Burgess.

He's come a long way from the Ashworth Hall council estate where he started life, the only son of jobbing printer, Clifford, and cleaner, Betty, who died quite recently.

However, he believes that his humble childhood was probably the making of him.

"I owe a tremendous debt to the Cull Valley. Everything about the place from the light and landscape to the warm people has had a terrific influence on me. I hope that comes across in my film. Dad was always there for me and encouraged me to do justice to myself in my studies. I've been in the right place at the right time on a few occasions in my life but I've always seized the opportunities that were on offer," he says.

His lifestyle is a reflection of that modest outlook. Tom is a private family man who lives quietly in London with his wife, Rachel, a social worker, and young children, David and Andrea. Does he have big ambitions for them, I wonder?

"Andrea's a bit of a drama queen, and wants to be an actress. But David has a very open mind. As long as he makes it to the Spurs first team, he doesn't mind what position they choose to play him," he laughs.

So what next for the man who is being tipped to become a leading player in the British film industry? Or does Hollywood beckon?

"I really don't think that would be my bag at all," he says, "although who knows in the distant future? Certainly, my next feature film will be here, in fact almost entirely in the Cull Valley. And once again, as with *Holiday Stories*, I'm going to be directing, and collaborating with Helena on an original screenplay."

"What can you tell us about it, or is it too early to be giving much away?"

"Well, I can say this much, it will be very different film from *Holiday Stories*. It's a thriller and altogether much darker. Two of the main characters are journalists, and it's got a working title of *Read All About Us*, although the way things work that won't make it through to production."

"So you can take the boy out of the Cull Valley, but you'll never take the Cull Valley out of the boy," I say as I put my pen and notepad away.

"Who'd want to?" he smiles. "This is the place that made me. It will always have a special place in my heart."

STORIES....JEANNIE DERBY....

"Does Teddy Beresford still work at the Valley Gazette?" Tom Waterfall wanted to know. *"We were mates back in primary school days,"* he told me, *"but rather lost touch after we went to different grammar schools."*

Tom was very keen to talk about his old chum.

"There was something a bit vulnerable about him, I always thought, a tendency to cave in under pressure. I first saw it in a Cubs' football match where he made a real pig's ear of a vital penalty kick even though the opposition goalkeeper was useless."

I reminded Tom that I'd once interviewed Rachel for a voxpop, and that she'd mentioned a tennis match in which he had beaten Teddy.

"That's one of life's Kodak moments for me," he said. *"I can see it now. Teddy blew a match point and I thought, it's like that time when he lost it in the Cubs, I can go on and beat him."*

I was apprehensive about meeting Tom as he's such a high-flyer, and films aren't really anything I know that much about. I'd done some homework before the interview which is why I was able to throw in Alan Parker and Ridley Scott. But I needn't have worried; Tom was really lovely and very unpretentious.

"Were you ambitious as a child?" I asked him.

"Not at all," he said. *"To be honest I didn't think that people from my sort of background could expect to achieve much. Dad tried to instil some sense of pride but Mum was too busy struggling to get by to offer that much encouragement. When I got into Cambridge, all she said was: "It can't be that hard if you've done it."*

"The tennis match must have been a big day for you," I said.

"I truly think it was one of life's turning points for me. My history teacher, Colin Sangster, made a surprising call that kept me in the match and I just went for it. And it wasn't just tennis. Something changed quite radically that afternoon; it was my perception of myself and my self-esteem. Suddenly, I was the crowd's favourite, with generous applause for all my best shots, and groans on the few occasions they didn't quite come off. Dad had told me that I could be one of life's winners if I really wanted to and I think that was the first day I believed it."

"Did you know that the umpire called it wrong?"

"I thought so but, because I wasn't absolutely certain, I decided to accept my good fortune. Throughout my life, I've tried to play things reasonably straight. But it's a tough old world and there are moments when some pragmatism or real-politik does no harm if you're going to get on. The irony, I dare say, is that I learned that lesson at the expense of Teddy Beresford, who was – I dare say still is – one of the nice guys."

"He is, I'm very fond of him," I assured Tom. "But it can't just come down to that tennis match, surely?"

"You're right, Jeannie," he said. "Obviously it's fanciful to suggest that I owe everything I've achieved to an incident on the court getting on for two decades ago. There would no doubt have been some different epiphany in my university years. I've got where I am today through sound application of what talent I was born with, sheer graft and occasional good luck. But Teddy Beresford didn't half, by accident rather than design, helped me to achieve lift off."

The National Diary

From our files

How others see us....

A recent survey revealed that our young people, boys in particular, are choosing to stay at home far longer. That Italian phenomenon – the Mammone – is becoming increasingly common in England. Professor Antonella Conte, of Bologna University, saw it coming...

'Mammone, you're making eyes at me'

My love affair with England was well under way when I met Teddy.

I might have got an idealised view of the country from books, films and pop music, but Teddy did nothing to stop me seeing our Anglo-Saxon cousins through rose-tinted spectacles.

He came into Keats' House, near the Spanish Steps. I had a part-time job there during my summer vacation from the University of Bologna, where I was a post-graduate student of physics. Teddy had a gorgeous mop of fair hair which he played with self consciously as he asked me in Italian for his ticket. I teased him by saying something very quickly. He looked charmingly all at sea for a second or two until I switched to English, and told him that my lunch break was coming up soon.

Teddy was a reporter with his local newspaper in Yorkshire. He was in his mid-20s and he shared a flat with another journalist. There was nothing macho about him; he had a self-deprecating manner quite unlike that of Italian boys I had dated. He was also very cultured, and knew as much about the Futurists, post-war Italian cinema and the Risorgimento as I did. I said I'd love to visit England, and I'd heard that Yorkshire was very beautiful. Perhaps made a little braver by the carafe of wine we were sharing, he took the hint.

I arrived in his market town about a month later. I remember saying to him: "Teddy, 'Exroyd and Hainsley are so peaceful", and he thought this was very funny. We had a blissful couple of days in his flat before, on the Sunday, he took me to his parents' house for lunch.

"What's in the bag?" I said, as we got into his car. He'd got more luggage than I'd arrived with from Rome and we were only travelling a few miles.

"It's my washing," he said. "I always take it over on a Sunday."

"Every Sunday?"

"Yes. I haven't got a machine, so it's better than using a laundrette."

If Teddy's Mama allowed him to do this, I imagined that she would be overbearing and protective, and I steeled myself for a tough afternoon. But I was wrong. She couldn't have made me feel more welcome. She even encouraged me to go and say hello to Maria Hopkinson, the Italian mother of his friend, Paul.

"Eric and Maria have been married very happily for 30 years," Valerie said.

Well, green light for me and for Italians in general, I decided. Valerie obviously wasn't the sort of Mama who was going to fight me for custody of her son. But you've probably guessed how the story unfolds.

"Teddy," I said to him when we were in bed back at his funny little flat. "Don't you love me just a leetle." He just shuffled and went back to sleep.

I wrote 'Ti amo' in shaving foam on his mirror, so he'd find it after I'd gone, but he never made any reference to it in his letters. He made vague promises to come to Rome again soon. But he never did. I suppose I'd known all along that he wasn't ready to settle down.

I often wonder what happened to him. Did Mama put her foot down and tell him to stop treating her house like a hotel? Did he marry a local girl, and stay on the local paper, so he could always be close to Mama?

Now we are learning that all over England, more young men are staying at home, just like all those Mammoni do here. They go to the local university, keep their old friends and part-time jobs, rely on Mama and Papa for everything and then, suddenly, they've reached 30 and they've never moved on.

Just like Teddy. I thought I'd found my English soul-mate. But in the end, perhaps there was just too much of the Italian in you, Teddy.

Still, I'll never forget you, my lovely Anglo-Saxon boy. Spero che sia molto felice. I 'ope you are very 'appy.

Julia's Journal

Anthony's always been very tolerant of my little flings, bless. But he's creating an awful fuss now. Maybe it's because I've mentioned babies and the need to make a new start with another man.

"You'd be fucking useless with one of them, a baby I mean," he says, when I bring up the subject over a G&T. "In fact, if there's a person in this world who'd be more useless with a bairn than your mother was, then I'm probably looking at her. But if it's what you want, don't let me stop you. It's just not going to happen on my watch. And if lover boy Teddy is willing to put you up the spout, don't let me stop him. Just so long, when it happens, that you're out of this house and gone forever."

"It might not have come to this if you'd been able to give me a baby, you SEXLESS SHIT."

Sometimes you have to raise your voice a little to get through to Anthony.

"I might well be a sexless shit, as you so charmingly put it," he says, "but you are too bonkers to have a baby. You're a fucking nutter, you couldn't possibly look after it, and you know this. You've known it since before we were married. We're stuck with one another, but it's just the two of us and that's how it's going to stay...unless Teddy takes you on."

"He will, you'll see."

"Sure he will, the day Park Avenue win the Premier League."

He slams the door on me. The G&T goes down the hatch in one. I put the glass down, roll up my sleeve and start to pick at my scars.

I hope he's not right about Teddy. I'm having to put an awful lot of pressure on him recently. Sex is a powerful weapon and he can't get enough of me. I've been threatening to withdraw my

179

favours unless he takes me on, and I thought that might do the trick. Unfortunately, he's showing signs of trying to resist me, though he's not managed it so far. He's always liked having sex with me at his parents' house, especially since his horrible mother Valerie made it so clear she disliked me, and overnights were ruled out. I think Teddy gets really turned on by the danger that we might be found out, should they return home while I'm there, especially as he's still clinging to the belief that they think our relationship is platonic.

But he tries to draw a line now and then, and said that sneaking in for stopovers was not on. On one occasion I did this recently. I let myself into his house after midnight; I'd recently discovered that there was a spare key in the rockery. I took it and got into bed with him.

"You bloody fruit cake," he said. "Suppose my dad had been taking one of late-night trips to the lavvy."

"Well, he wasn't," I said, taking a peek down his jim-jams. "Very nice. I can be gone before they get up, Big Boy," I said to him.

As I always do, I got my own way in the end, but getting that commitment is proving more elusive. To make matters worse, his newspaper is on the verge of a wave of redundancies.

"We can't live on love," he told me. "If I get the push, there's no way I'll be able to support the two of us, let alone think about buying one of those fancy Barrowclough Mill apartments."

He's been using this one for a while now. The Gazette must be going through the most protracted redundancy process in the history of British industry. God knows what sort of system they've got for deciding who's going and who's staying. I'm beginning to wonder whether there really are any job losses coming up at all.

"You'd better shape up," I told him. "If I don't get some commitment soon, you won't get so much as a blow job in the charity shop's stockroom."

Monday July 13 2009

Window smashed

Police were called to Geneva Row, Ainsley, on Saturday morning when a garage window was smashed in an unsuccessful, attempted break-in.

STORIES...GAVIN....

If you looked through today's paper, you would also have come across single paragraphs accompanied by the headlines 'Coffee morning', 'Show rehearsal' and 'Club meeting'.

People sometimes ask me why such minor events should appear in the paper at all. Some pars could, at a pinch, be said to provide a social service or to act as an information board. However, you could equally argue that everyone required at the show rehearsal will have been told, and that it's of no interest to anyone else.

As often as not, these pieces are just space fillers, and fillers are exactly what we call them.

I was doing the police calls and the Force's press liaison officer mentioned the smashed garage window in passing. Thrower said that we needed a few fillers and I gave him the window plus a couple of car break-ins. There are only six houses in Geneva Row, and when Teddy came into work on the Monday morning I asked him if he had seen anything.

"It was our place, Gav."

It turned out that the culprit was Julia Yates. Philip and Valerie had gone to Ljubljana for the weekend, Julia had somehow got wind that Teddy was home alone and turned up on the Saturday morning.

"Slightly spooky. I don't think I even mentioned their trip, so God knows how she found out."

"Some kind of woman's instinct maybe?"

"Who knows, she's a strange cove, Gav."

"She's like the Universe."

"You'll have to narrow that one down a little."

"Not just stranger than we know, stranger than we can know," I said.

"She's odd all right, and no one's going to accuse her of being noticeably perceptive, or having much sense of humour. But there's a weird animal instinct going on there which enables her to get to the bottom of anything which in any way relates to herself and her own life."

"So what happened when Julia arrived on Saturday?"

"I was still in bed when the doorbell rang," he said. "I wasn't up for it so I decided to lie low and pretend I'd not heard."

"But how did she actually come to smash the window?" I asked.

"It must have been sheer bloody frustration, she kept knocking on the door then went to the rockery to get the key, but it wasn't there because I'd moved it after the last time she pulled that stroke. I continued to ignore her, then heard the sound of breaking glass. I dashed downstairs in my dressing gown, grabbed her and pulled her inside."

"How exciting," I said.

"Yeah, the fun was just beginning, because a few minutes later we've got a copper knocking. Seems next door called 999 and a car must have been in the neighbourhood."

"The Police, hey? Always there when you don't want them."

"So I kept Julia under wraps and told the officer that I'd seen a young lad running off in the direction of the park."

"Honesty's always the best policy."

"I was reluctant to admit that my girlfriend was hysterical."

"And meanwhile, she was doing all sorts of mad things like setting fire to your kitchen."

"Not quite. She'd gone into a kind of trance, she was looking at the cut on her arm that she'd aggravated and was making a curious flapping movement with her other hand, as if she was encouraging the ink to dry on a piece of paper. Her face was drained of all expression and I wondered if she'd had some kind of fit. When I was a kid I saw a neighbour's dog – he was called Argonaut for some reason – shaking violently, rolling its eyes and foaming at the mouth. 'See this, Edward', my dad said. 'When people have epileptic fits, this is exactly what it looks like'."

"But I take it Julia didn't look like Argonaut?"

"Not at all," said Teddy. "She just looked like herself, though devoid of expression. The cut didn't look that bad but I thought I'd better get her down to A&E in case she needed a stitch or two."

"Was she contrite?"

"Not really, it was like nothing much had happened, she was banging on again about buying a flat. If I ever hear the words 'Barrowclough Mill apartments' again, I'll fucking scream. 'Great time to buy,' she says. 'Wonderful investment, much more affordable now the price has gone down,' she adds. 'Still room to negotiate further on the price,' she advises."

" 'And room for me to move in with you as soon as you're comfortably installed', she envisages."

"Exactamundo."

"Do you think you might just have bitten off more than you can chew?"

"Right again, you are on the money today, Gav."

"You'll to have to give her the hard word, you know."

"I know, I know, I'm bracing myself."

"Perhaps you could use the garage window as a starting point," I suggested. "You know, we need some cooling-off time, kind of thing."

"That ain't going to work. The funny thing was, she rang yesterday and it was like the incident had never happened at all."

"Like a cartoon character," I suggested.

"How do you mean?"

"Well, pulverised, burned to a cinder or shredded, but returning undamaged for the next frame."

"You could put it that way," he smiled, though the analogy appealed to him more than the situation.

"Phew," I said. "Rather you than me."

CULL VALLEY EVENING GAZETTE

Wednesday July 15 2009

A Walk on the mild side

Ingenious solution out of Africa

Our columnist and middle-aged fogey Kenneth 'Chuck' Thrower takes a light-hearted look at the way we live today, as he recalls more innocent times, and tackles the politically-correct brigade

Remember Miss Africa South? Her name was Pearl Jansen and she was the lovely coloured girl who took the runner-up spot when she represented her country in the 1970 Miss World contest.

Her country, of course, was South Africa. Pearl was unable to enter as Miss South Africa because an equally gorgeous white girl already held that title.

I was in my late teens when that happened. I didn't really understand much about apartheid then but I was struck by how sensible it was to have a 'two beauty queens solution'. Remarkable, was it not, that the organisers of a mere beauty contest were able to make people sit up and think in a way that numerous sporting bodies, with their infantile ban on South African participation, had failed to do?

And yet, and yet…even as I write these words I can hear the grumblings of discontent from our more liberal readers. They will be sharpening their pens as they prepare to wage war on silly, well-meaning Chuck through our readers' letters columns.

Some will grumble that the coloured lady was forced unfairly to invert the name of her country. But, for God's sake, the whites – wrongly, we know – ruled the land. They were hardly likely to agree to a Caucasian Miss Africa South, and a coloured Miss South Africa. Even having a coloured Lady in the competition at all was a starting point. How many other nations were given two bites at the cherry in such a prestigious event? (Miss United Kingdom North and Miss United Kingdom South?) Surely this was positive discrimination. I argued in 1970 that, one day, we might even have a coloured Miss South Africa – and, by gum, I was proved right.

As for those miserable moaning minnies who object to beauty contests *per se*, the less said the better. They have had their way, of course, relegating the events to sideshows on satellite television. They are the same people who destroyed that other icon of post-war British innocence, *The Black and White Minstrel Show*.

And who, precisely, are these people? I'm tempted, like Peter Finch in *Network*, to ask you all to go to the window, open it wide and shout to the world: "I'm as mad as hell and I'm not going to take it any more…from the politically correct brigade!"

That's right. The PC brigade. They want to tell us how to think, how to lead our lives, which foreign countries to visit (if any, all that precious fuel being wasted etc, etc) and which jokes we can laugh at (in other words only PC jokes that aren't actually funny, I hear you saying, and I wouldn't disagree). Okay, this has been said before and sometimes, I must admit, by yours truly.

The bird of common sense has long since flown from the nest of life. But when I opened an old reference book last weekend and saw a picture of Pearl Jansen, it brought a smile across my face which (for width, if not beauty) matched that of the beaming features of Miss Africa South and the other top four girls from the 1970 final at London's Royal Albert Hall. (For the record, the competition was won by Jennifer Huston, Miss Grenada, a 22-year-old air hostess, while the Misses Israel, Sweden and South Africa finished third, fourth and fifth respectively).

No members of the International Political Correctness Politburo were, as far as I can make out, on the panel of judges.

Ah, yes. Those of us with long memories can smile a little wistfully as we remember those days of innocence when the lovely Pearl Jansen, Miss Africa South, showed us a gentler way to challenge attitudes and change the world for the better.

STORIES....KENNETH THROWER.....

Yes, a few of the Cull Valley bleeding heart liberals had a go at me over that column, even though I pulled my punches, and our favourite sub-editor had toned it down in a couple of places.

The trouble with the PC brigade like our friend Mr Beresford is that they want it both ways; censorship is one of their weapons of choice but they are quite happy to complain about censorship or tampering with the evidence if it doesn't fit with their view of the world.

I'll give you a good example. There was a hoo-ha the other week over an American advertisement that had been digitally altered for consumption in Poland. Three businessmen were sitting at a desk, and the middle one, a balding and kindly-looking bespectacled fella, like your favourite uncle, was black. When the advert appeared in Poland his face had been replaced by a white one. (Incidentally, they'd forgotten to change his hands, which were still black!)

Because it suited their agenda, the PC brigade went ballistic about what they considered a form of censorship. But, and this might surprise you, I do believe that, in this case, they were for once (it does happen, like stopped clocks) absolutely right. That face switch was true racism, pandering to the Poles' prejudices.

In any case, if all the black people we meet were like that nice man in the advert, we wouldn't have anything to worry about, would we?

TEDDY

I sense that another of life's sod the *National Diary* moments approaches…

…This is the most epic and mind-blowing thing that has happened to me for years, no ever….

…I took some flowers round for Ruth a few days ago. Rory had told me that she was very down.

"Remember the time I bought you the Michaelmas daisies?" Ruth said, smiling sadly, as she went in search of a vase. "I thought it was very sweet the way you kept them after being told about Rory and me."

"I tried to hate Rory's guts but couldn't quite manage it," I said.

"You know, Teddy," she said, "We've always appreciated the way that you've never asked us about babies. People can be so insensitive with their questions."

To be honest, I'm not certain that I'd given the matter much thought until quite recently. Most men that I've come across only agree to have babies because they want the women who want the babies. Only after they do become dads does it dawn on them that they are genuinely pleased. My guess had always been that Ruth saw enough of kids at school, and Rory was grateful that he didn't have to go through all that parenting stuff. It's only during the past year that they've both confided in me this yearning. There might have been vague, earlier hints that babies had not been ruled out – "We'll have to see if circumstances mean we can really manage a foreign holiday next year," or whatever – but nothing more concrete.

Now they had both decided that it was time to get confessional on a big scale.

"The monthly cycle of anticipation, hope and disappointment is awful," said Ruth. "If anything, it's got worse since I went and jumped the gun by telling Hazel our 'good news' which turned out to be nothing of the sort."

"You talked about it before you got wed," I said, recalling a pub conversation sparked by a couple who had walked in with young twins.

"Naturally enough," said Ruth, "We'd discussed babies then. We don't have secrets. We agreed that, if either of us got broody, the other would go along with it, and that is pretty much what happened. The idea of motherhood just crept up on me, from something that might be worth considering after all, to a faint sense of loss that something was missing when I saw young mums with a pram to, finally, what I can only describe as a pressing need. I want more than anything to be a mum."

"What about you, Rory?" I asked.

"I feel pretty much the same way now," he said, putting an arm round her. Which is why we wanted to talk to you today."

"Me?"

"It's alright, nothing to be frightened about," said Ruth, noting a look of panic in my eyes.

"The bottom line is this," said Rory. "As things stand we can't have kids."

"As things stand?"

"Is this to do with your ovarian cyst, Ruth? I thought you got an all-clear."

"No, it's not" said Rory, "We did. It's to do with me."

"You're firing blanks, you mean."

"Crikey, give it to me straight...but as makes no odds, that's more or less it."

"So..." they both said, and there was an awkward silence.

"Have you thought of adopting?" I said, although as soon as it came out of my mouth I wanted to put it back in again. I wouldn't have been summoned to be told that. I knew what was coming.

Ruth said: "You've got to go through all sorts of hoops these days before you're deemed suitable material to take on someone else's child. We've had a plan B for some time, and although there are a few avenues to go down first, we reckon that plan B could be, erm.."

"...A good short cut," offered Rory.

"And Plan B is?"

Rory gulped before delivering Plan B; the moment had come up sooner in the conversation than he'd envisaged.

"We'd ask a close friend to be a sperm donor."

"Right."

"You, obviously, Teddy," he added.

"What do you think?" said Ruth. "I know it's a lot to ask but it seems like the perfect solution in so many ways."

"Blimey." My head was spinning, from this out-of-the-blue revelation. Surely my only answer could be yes. This was a chance for a form of eternity, without the responsibility; though that was hardly a noble reason for agreeing to be a sperm donor.

"Well, I'm incredibly flattered, honoured even, needless to say."

Rory and Ruth's faces dropped, as if they thought those words were my preface to 'but no…'

"I just think that this is such a big issue, it's got to be something I sleep on."

Rory can be quite tough when he gets the bit between his teeth. I knew he was thinking what's to mull over, how can you have any doubts? Ruth laid a restraining hand on him. She was also keeping a stiff upper lip. Maybe she was disappointed by my less-than-totally enthusiastic response. Or maybe she was determined to keep the tears at bay so that I couldn't accuse her of emotional blackmail. Then again, perhaps she knew me well enough to understand that I didn't make big decisions easily and often ended up making the wrong one anyway. If I had to go away and sit in a dark room before coming to the only possible and sensible conclusion, so be it.

As I drove home, a strange sensation crept over me, a thought I'd never had before. Rory Nolan's low sperm count made him the end of a line that had stretched from the beginnings of time; from life-forms emerging out of the primordial swamp to the first humans in Africa, who gradually made their way north to the European land mass, eventually fetching up in Ireland. There his ancestors prospered or more likely eked out a subsistence-level living through the generations, survived by the skin of their teeth in the face of disease and famine, the arrival of Cromwell's bloody crew, the Black and Tans, the civil war of the 1920s, and while we're at it let's not forget the misery heaped on them by the dead hand of the Catholic Church.

So what does Rory's grandfather do? He hoves up empty-handed in 1950s' England with a wife and three kids, searching for accommodation (sorry mate, no Darkies, no Irish in this gaff) and a better life, digs roads, repairs railways and runs a market stall. Their youngest son is especially bright and makes his way up in the world, via grammar school and university, marries a nice middle-class English girl and moves into suburbia. "Welcome to the neighbourhood, Mr and Mrs Nolan."… "Oh you're an accountant, Mr Nolan, very nice." No one's calling anyone a thick Paddy any more. Rory turns up around the mid 1970s, a smart chip off the old block, but that's it. Thanks to a genetic quirk of fate he's the end of the line, just when things were turning out so well for the Nolans. Fin d'histoire…

Except that he isn't. Maybe the reason I've never had these thoughts before is because they are so bloody stupid and literal. If producing offspring is your way of leaving something behind, all you've got to do is impregnate a teenage girl on the Meadow Croft Estate and move on.

Rory *is* going to continue the Nolan line. And he will do that by being a dad, it doesn't matter a fig to him whether he's the biological father. He just wants to bring up a child as his own with Ruth. And that kid will have a lot going for it. Rory and Ruth, what better people to have as parents? The toddler will be first out of the starting trap, immediately ahead of the field as he or she begins the first lap of life's marathon.

It will be good for Rory and Ruth to know that little Nolan comes from good, integrity-packed stock on the biological father's side. They might have had some doubts about a sperm donor of whom they knew very little. Suppose they'd got a donor who, unknown to them, had some less-than-appealing character traits. Suppose they'd ended up with the sort of man who engages in unsavoury business; activities such as, for the sake of argument, going into their home to pick up the mail and water the plants when they are away, and using it for a 'quickie' with a married girlfriend. Or realising that he really must end his relationship with this girlfriend, but continuing to come back for one last frolic because he's so penis happy.

Put like that, it wasn't so much a matter of whether I should be thinking about doing something for Rory and Ruth; more a case of did I merit the faith that they had placed in me?

It didn't take me that long to come to my senses. I'd also been thinking about the *National Diary* in which I'd revealed that I'd like to be a dad one day. No, not quite; my exact words, if I remember correctly, were more along the lines of "I wouldn't mind being a dad one day. If I never find the right woman perhaps I could at least be a sperm donor." What was that all about? Put like that it sounds like nothing more than vanity. No, I would make myself an important part of little Nolan's life.

I phoned to apologise for my hesitation and to say, not in so many words, that the Beresford seed was at their disposal. Ruth burst into tears, and so did I. There would be some finer points to iron out later, such as at what point in the future, if ever, the kid is told who his biological father is. But I knew I'd made a good decision.

We all got very relaxed about it once I'd made my mind up; we don't need to go into the finer details of the reading matter that accompanied my contribution to Project Baby Nolan.

191

At Sunday lunch, Rory said to me: "We were both worried that you might think being a sperm donor involved having sex with Ruth. I assured her that you'd know what a baster baby was."

"I wasn't so sure," said Ruth. "The kitchen's not your natural battleground is it, Teddy?"

"Even I've come across basters and I can rustle up a decent meal," I said, slightly offended by the notion that I was clueless on the catering front. "You could have said to me: 'this wonderful piece of low-tech kitchen equipment, together with a little help from you, might be the answer to all our problems'."

"Using a *new* baster, of course," said Rory. "We don't want to conceive something that's half lamb – or beef or pork come to that'. Seriously, you'll be great in a hands-on uncle kind of role, Teddy."

"I wonder what Julia would make of it?" said Ruth, bringing us back from base comedy to the real world within two sentences.

"She's not going to find out, is she?" I said.

"Of course she isn't," said Ruth. "We'll almost certainly keep the sperm donation business to ourselves. For the time being, at least."

"I'd like to see Julia's reaction if you did tell her," said Rory.

"Don't even think about it," said Ruth.

"The winding-down process is on, we're on the verge of splitting up, in any case," I said. "Really on the verge. There's no need for her to even know that you're pregnant."

"Thank God for that," said Ruth. "Sorry, I know it sounds awful, but she's really not for you, Teddy. Have you decided how you're going to break it to her?"

"Not really, I'm just going to busk it. It might be better if I leave it until after Apfelbaum's anniversary next month."

"Yeah, thanks again for landing us with that one," said Rory.

"No, that's not fair, Rory," said Ruth. "Teddy asked for some moral support and we agreed not to give her the cold shoulder."

"As part of this winding-down process," said Rory, who was on the verge of getting seriously pissed off with me.

"When the moment arrives, be careful exactly what you say," said Ruth, ignoring him and turning to me.

"Sorry? What do you mean?"

"Just stick to the point, Teddy, and be as gentle as possible. Don't get waylaid by irrelevancies such as Rory and me disliking her. No point pretending otherwise among ourselves, but it's neither here nor there as far as you and Julia are concerned."

"Right, Ruth," I said, giving her a little salute.

"Sorry to be a bossy-boots. Sometimes you're so lacking in guile I worry about what you'll come out with. You've never been someone who gets away with little indiscretions."

Was this a veiled reference to my use of their house for country matters? Might have been, might not.

"It's a nice quality by and large, Teddy," she reassured me, but just tread carefully."

Julia's Journal

Things could be going better with Teddy. The trouble is that we've been down this road before, just the once a few years ago when I got, allegedly, too close to one of my admirers. There was a confrontation involving his wife, and I think the police might have been called in at one point with some talk about the need for me to keep my distance.

We don't need to worry about that now, but I can remember the very point at which that relationship started to go into reverse, the admirer saying he didn't want to get in too deep. Under pressure from dangerous outside elements. And we had a similar moment with Teddy the other day.

We were in a Starbucks near the multiplex on his lunchtime break. Rory and Ruth were going away for a long weekend and I'd suggested we might spend the evening at their place.

"That won't be possible," he said.

"Why not?"

"I haven't got a key."

"I thought they always gave you a key when they went away."

"Well, not this time."

"Why not."

"It's only a short break," he said, hesitantly.

"Even so, it's peculiar because they usually ask you to keep an eye on the house."

"I'd have thought it was obvious why," he said.

"You'll have to tell me."

"I think they might have their suspicions about last time."

"What about last time?" I was getting very impatient with him now.

"They've only tolerated our overnights because they were told you've got an open marriage. And it's one thing our coming to the house when they're there, another when they're not."

"What's the difference, we've done it before. It's pretty clear they don't like me that much."

Teddy said nothing.

"You're not going to stick up for me?" I said, raising my voice for the first time.

"It's not that they don't like you so much as they're not sure we are a very good combo," he managed eventually.

"You mean, I'm not good enough for you?"

"No I don't mean that and they agreed to go to Apfelbaum with us tomorrow."

"On sufferance, no doubt."

"Let's all try to get on, and have a nice evening together," he said. "Before we go, I'm taking a few pictures of us in their garden with my new digital camera."

"That's good timing at least, as I'm having my hair done in the morning."

"That's nice," he said, although I couldn't imagine what difference it made to him. "And I'm going to York for the day on Thursday. You might like to come along."

I pulled a face.

"It's a great city, and some fine shops, too," he added. "Although you'll have to remember that it's a kind of working day for me because I'm doing a write-up for a Gazette travel supplement."

"Teddy Beresford goes to York, Kenneth Thrower sees Rome," I said.

"Fucking hell, you're hard work sometimes," he said. "Look," he added more gently again, "You'll have a nice day, I promise."

"I suppose it will be better than Greenwood bloody Crags," I conceded.

195

"How are you going to handle this one, Lady?" I asked myself later. Rory and Ruth's key is the second to slip from my grasp, following the removal of the one under the rockery. You're in danger of losing your touch.

It could have been a worse morning, though. I was tempted to ask Teddy why he never got a copy of Rory and Ruth's key cut; we could have gone there any time we liked. I'm not sure that would have been well received. Teddy has strong notions of loyalty to friends, even when they have done nothing to deserve them.

These are all temporary setbacks. As I've said before, I get my way in the end.

The National Diary

July 2009

The camera never lies

Readers' photographs: Today, Teddy Beresford examines an image of three friends, captured before a night-out at a restaurant

It takes me a while to embrace new technology; it's a standing joke among friends that I only carry my mobile phone on special occasions. This picture was taken the other night with my first digital camera.

The couple are my close friends Rory and Ruth Nolan. The blonde, sporting a new hair-do, is my girlfriend, Julia. It's one of about half a dozen snaps I took in Rory and Ruth's garden, in front of Rory's attempts at topiary, before the four of us set off together for a meal at my favourite restaurant, Apfelbaum.

As ever, Rory and Ruth appear very relaxed and happy together. Standing a little apart from them, Julia does look lovely. She's very photogenic. The camera really likes her, or maybe it's the other way round.

What makes the image significant is the half-dozen snaps I took either side of this shot. On those pictures, Rory and Ruth's expressions and poses are constantly changing ever so slightly, as though they're reacting to a joke that they've just 'got', or because something off camera has caught their attention. But Julia's perfect smile is identical in every picture. She's decided that it's the one that works best, and she's sticking to it. It's her 'look at me' pose. She might as well be the only person in the picture; there's not the slightest sense of any interaction with anyone else, all that matters is that she looks good. In that sense, the image of Julia is like a throw-back to the early days of photography, when people were forced to adopt a certain pose and hold on – so it must have seemed – indefinitely while the camera did its work. Julia would have made the perfect model for a Victorian cameraman.

My camera was passed from Julia to Rory and finally to Ruth.

"Rory's sprouted a pair of green wings," Ruth said, looking at the two bushes that appeared to be emerging from his shoulders.

Rory and I laughed. Julia came out with a funny, perplexed little smile which indicated to me that she hadn't seen the joke. Ruth eyed her with interest, as she'd been doing all afternoon and I suddenly realised what she was thinking: Julia hadn't noticed Rory's 'wings' because she'd never looked at anyone else on the picture; she was only interested in the image of herself.

Saturday July 25 2009

The apple of our eye

Hazel Moses revisits Apfelbaum, which has long been one her favourite restaurants

Apfelbaum has picked up a clutch of gongs under the ten-year stewardship of Garry Ellison and his German wife, Ursula.

They have been in the *Good Food Guide* for at least half of that period and it's great to report that there is no sign of Garry and Uschi, as she likes to be known, resting on their laurels. An evening meal at Apfelbaum (German for apple tree) is as much a treat as it was when my husband, Jim, brought me here on our first date.

We visited last Friday, and Apfelbaum was busier than ever, because of the anniversary, fully booked and with a few people who turned up 'on spec', surely more in hope than expectation, being turned away.

Garry and Uschi really like to make you feel at home. There are lovely little touches, such as the bread rolls and coloured butter, both home-made and served alongside our complimentary appetiser drink, a shot of peach juice and vanilla cream with a hint of schnapps. Weird but wonderful, somehow it works.

Apfelbaum is classy, but it's also unpretentious. I love the colourful décor and its centrepiece, the crazy, deliberately kitsch mural (the work of Garry who has a degree in fine art) of a Bavarian village inn, with men in Lederhosen drinking frothing steins of lager served by comely wenches. And there's a Germanic influence in the menu, which usually includes one hearty pork dish, and apfel strudel. However, Apfelbaum might best be described as modern European. I started with a linguini and sardines dish, which also featured saffron threads, dried chillies and pine nuts. It had a lively, zingy taste.

Jim, who was already in heaven because he had discovered that Apfelbaum now serves hand-pumped Cockcroft's Golden Accelerator, pronounced himself perfectly satisfied with his prawn cocktail. I heard an acquaintance who was sitting a couple of seats away make some rather sniffy comment about Jim's selection. "No, this is great," he said to me, and I learned that several big-name chefs are fans of the dish. That was, I must admit, a surprise to me, as was prawn cocktail's appearance on the Apfelbaum menu, but Uschi has breathed new life into that old favourite. With the right ingredients – Uschi revealed to me that her special recipe includes brandy, creamed horseradish and double cream mixed in with her home-made tomato ketchup – it's a starter fit for a king.

Jim tells me that prawn cocktail was the starter dish of choice for most footballers during the 1980s. (Boys will be boys. I've no idea how he can possibly know such a thing!).

Jim maintained a maritime theme for mains. He tucked into his pan-fried lemon sole, so fresh he said that it might have leapt from trawler to table, like a man who hadn't eaten for weeks. Anyone would think I didn't feed him properly!

I relished my braised shoulder of lamb which was perfection, served with vegetables that were spot-on, just a tad undercooked as they should be. I hope, incidentally, that the lamb on my plate had enjoyed a frolicking and happy, if short, life. I'm a committed carnivore, but lamb will always be one of my guilty pleasures. I think it comes down to the time Jim took me to the Lake District, and a couple of sweet lambs pressed their little noses against the hotel window!

As Jim was not going to be deflected from his Golden Accelerator, I settled for a large glass of the house white wine, a decent Chilean Chardonnay which was crisp and fresh with a hint of lemongrass.

Our waitress must have had a sweet tooth because she was keen to recommend all the desserts and that great English favourite, sticky toffee pudding, the only possible choice for me, did not disappoint. Jim went for a passion fruit flan, which exploded with flavour, and a scoop of home-made vanilla ice-cream, which really did taste of vanilla.

The service was how I like it, attentive and friendly but not too in-your-face, and the bill, around the £80 mark, was pretty reasonable when you consider the quality of the food.

Apfelbaum remains the best show in town as far as I'm concerned, a place to go when you've really got something to celebrate with the people who matter most to you. And if anyone starts questioning a menu that includes prawn cocktail among the starters, make sure you put them in their place!

STORIES...HAZEL...

"It's not exactly Jay Rayner is it, dear?" some patronising smart-arse (I almost betrayed my London roots by saying southern smart-arse) observed after reading one of my restaurant reviews.

I dare say that it isn't (and I'll admit I can get a bit gushy, such as the time I wrote about Rory Nolan's blue eyes) but Jay Rayner doesn't have to talk to a mother with a Downs Syndrome child, write about the latest daft diet fad and interview an apprentice female plasterer who's passed out with top marks at the local tech, all on the same day.

We're nothing if not versatile here, few journalists have the luxury of concentrating entirely on one area of expertise as you might on a national newspaper; some of us are specialists in all styles. Even our arts and entertainments man, Rufus, whose big thing is the theatre, has to write about everything from rock music and local poets to film and television.

So restaurant reviews are written pretty much by any journalist who is willing to sing for her supper with 700-800 words on an eating place, knocked out in her own time. It's a source of amusement to Jim that someone as basic as me in the kitchen should be pronouncing on the quality of restaurant food. Occasionally, there will be a sharp intake of breath from Kenneth Thrower when a reporter puts in an £80 plus expenses claim. That might explain the naff convention since time immemorial of saying who we dined with, and what they had to eat, as if to justify the outlay. Would any reader give a flying fart that I went for the linguini and sardines and it was Jim who opted for the prawn cocktail?

That reference to Jim's starter was about as far as I could go in having a dig at the wretched girl who dissed his choice. The universal prejudice against prawn cocktail isn't going to go away overnight, and neither is my distaste for Julia Yates. I didn't like Julia when I first met her and she didn't do anything to change my opinion the other night. I pulled a funny face at Jim when the four of them walked in: Teddy, Ruth, Rory and Julia, whose ever-so-slightly over-ripe complexion suggested that she was just on the turn.

"She's the Stepford Wife, albeit wasted on her husband," I told Jim, although he'd worked out that for himself, due to Teddy's presence.

"Not much of one, the entry model, perhaps," said Jim with uncharacteristic bitchiness; Julia doesn't exactly encourage a generosity of spirit.

"She's definitely that."

I waved to them. Rory and Ruth came over and said hello. It had been lovely to see them both again when I wrote about their work together. But I'd felt that there was an elephant in the room, with baby talk conspicuous by its absence. In Apfelbaum, however, Ruth was positively oozing happiness. I didn't ask, but it looked very promising.

Meanwhile, Teddy and Julia headed straight for their table, nodding in our direction as they did so – he sheepishly, she perfunctorily. Teddy has already been on the receiving end of a verbal lashing from Julia about his lack of commitment. He told me this at work, expecting sympathy; what he got was a water cooler talking-to about his intentions.

I overheard Rory, like Jim, going for the prawn cocktail, which prompted Julia to say: "I never dreamed that anyone with any semblance of taste touched that these days."

Rory didn't hold back.

"Actually, love, I think you'll find that both Brian Turner and Marco Pierre White have sung the praises of prawn cocktail, as long as it's made properly. I dare say their opinion counts for something."

Well, that shut her up, though she looked peeved about it. I'd hazard a guess that she's the kind of girl who's used to getting her own way. When will Teddy come to his senses?

I was bloody angry with him last year when he cried off from our little foursome with Sally. She made no comment, but I knew she was thinking: "Is this bloke the best you can come up with? I'll make my own arrangements in future."

I didn't buy Teddy's explanation, sinusitis or whatever, for a minute. You can always tell when he's not being straight. I can read his mind every bit as well as I can fathom Sally's, and I could almost see the cog wheels turning before he decided: "As I don't fancy you, the chances are I'll feel the same about your sister. Let's not put it to the test."

He looked rather ruefully at her picture when she did her speed-dating feature…."Too late, pal," I thought.

Julia's Journal

I was reading a newspaper profile of a famous lady politician the other day. You know, one of those things like a potted biography.

The writer mentioned the high and low points of her life, and this got me thinking about my own 'best of times' and 'worst of times'. You can take your pick in the second category, although they would have all involved Anthony.

Quite a catch, most people thought when they first met him, and I can still see the look of wonder on Mum and Dad's face when I turned up with Anthony. Unable to believe that their crazy daughter had finally attracted someone handsome, well established and upstanding.

He seemed to be the answer to all my problems. Someone to give me a decent life and quite attractive into the bargain. A bitchy acquaintance said: "If you've got to have a sugar daddy, darling, he'll do any time." "Too good to be true?" she added cattily.

She was right, as it transpired. I decided to withhold my favours long enough for Anthony to appreciate that I wasn't an easy lay. But he never even tried his luck. I'd met the perfect gentleman. Who would have thought, in this day and age, that a man would be opposed to pre-marital sex?

Call me naïve, but I took it all at face value. Which brings me to as good a choice for 'worst of times' as any. My wedding day. There I was, standing next to Anthony at the altar, thinking that I had made the biggest mistake of my life. I'd begun to get an inkling of where Anthony's real tastes lay and the honeymoon night confirmed my suspicions, although I initially hid my doubts. I wish I'd been more sparing with the details to Teddy. I almost felt disloyal to Anthony when I saw his reaction. "That's one of the most amazing stories I've ever heard," Teddy said.

That was in our early days when Teddy was like putty in my hands. Now he's giving me a few headaches with his resistance to my project. I'd like to think that baby and me in Barrowclough Mill will be among my 'best of times' one day. But getting Teddy on board is proving highly challenging, and Rory and Ruth are not making life any easier. When everything has been sorted out, right and proper, I shall ease the gruesome twosome out of the equation, no question. As I've said, I always get what I want and I most certainly do not want them under my roof, if they can't behave decently towards me when I'm a guest at their wretched barn.

What I can't stand is their cosy little way of making silly in-jokes with one another, which embrace Teddy but not me. There was a classic example in their garden before we went to the restaurant. Teddy was messing around with his new digital camera – his first, would you believe it, I thought everyone had one of them by now. He passed it round so we could all have a look at the pictures.

"Oh look," she says, "Rory's sprouted a pair of wings." And they all fall apart laughing! Fucking hilarious! What the hell's that all about?

Anyway, Apfelbaum was okay, though it's hardly the great shakes that Teddy makes out. I could swing for the bloke who did that ghastly Alpine mural. I told Teddy this and he said: "You might get a chance if he's in tonight. It's Uschi's husband." Come to think of it, the Moses girl – all lovey-dovey with her hubby a couple of tables away from us – is a big fan of Apfelbaum, too. I'm not so sure about her either, from what I've seen, but she's got good taste in domestic interiors, if nothing else. I could see from the way her eyes were popping that she was properly impressed with our house when I showed her round for her little *Through the Keyhole* column.

Rory revealed all the sophistication of the Oirish by ordering prawn cocktail. I made the mildest of observations about his selection and Ruth looked as if she wanted to strangle me.

Which was a pity in a way. I'd been making a real effort to be nice and, to be fair, they'd been perfectly pleasant as well. I'd even come up with a little joke when some reference was made to the chattering classes. I thought about this for a few seconds then said: "I thought they were naughty boys at school." Rory and Ruth both smiled even though I'm not sure they got the joke. Teddy said that I was a natural comedian.

"Comedienne," I corrected him, and Rory and Ruth smiled at that, a 'freebie' because I hadn't intended it as a joke.

The mood was quite upbeat and Rory seemed determined to behave well, as if in apology for his uncalled-for reaction to my prawn cocktail remark.

Teddy annoyed me the most; he was excessively interested in Ruth's welfare. She spent ten minutes in the lavatory at one point and Teddy kept asking if she was feeling alright. I started to wonder about Ruth's condition, she looked so kind of pleased with herself. And when Ruth told the waiter that she wanted a cranberry juice, Teddy reacted as if this was the most fascinating thing he'd heard all day. So if I am right about Ruth, Teddy must know or at least have some inkling already. You'd think he was going to be the dad himself he's being so, what's the word, solicitous.

The evening ended well enough, though. Teddy was driving and he dropped off Rory and Ruth first. They bid me good night in a civil manner.

On the way back to Green Pastures, I said to Teddy: "You were very concerned about Ruth." I hope I sounded sympathetic.

"Rory said she's been a little under the weather recently, that's all," he told me.

Teddy, I do believe you are telling me fibs, I thought, but merely said: "I'm looking forward to our day in York. I've got a shop wish-list."

"Yes, well..." he said and must have thought better of whatever was on his mind.

A strange evening and, when I looked back on it the following day, worrying. Teddy rather distant; Rory and Ruth quite tolerable despite a few cross words. Or had they been too nice? Was it the behaviour of two people who believe that, as I won't be part of Teddy's life — and therefore their own — for much longer, they might as well leave a good impression?

The National Diary

July 2009

Brittle Beresford won battles but blew war

Diary sports editor Jon Stretford recalls a momentous sporting encounter as he tours the German capital

To Berlin last week, that magnificent, turbulent European city which beckons us through something less tangible than beauty.

After a riotous night supping substantial quantities of Erdinger Weiss Bier it was breakfast at the Reichstag, and an open-top bus tour of the city to clear our heads. Our guide, the very model of a Prussian major general, indicated monuments to a couple of minor military triumphs.

"They won the friendlies, but lost the big wars," quipped one of the less hung-over members of our party.

We all roared our approval, before reflecting that, when it came to soccer, the ball has always been on the other Teutonic foot. How often has Germany's national team looked mediocre in non-competitive games, and then in the World Cup overcome superior opposition through a never-say-die work ethic, and an ability to bend the rules that little bit more decisively? Fans of the Beautiful Game will be haunted forever by the ghosts of Puskas's Hungary (1954), The Holland of Cruyff (1974) and Platini's France (1982 and 1986).

But at least we revere the memory of those sides and their near misses. What of those glorious teams whose early knock-outs in tournaments consign them to oblivion? Who now remembers the Soviet Union and the great Danes of 1986, or the Colombians of 1994, 5-0 conquerors of Argentina in Buenos Aires during the qualifiers, but whose bizarre defeat by the USA led directly to the gruesome death, in Medellin, of their ominously-named defender Andres Escobar?

All this came to mind recently when I read in Quidnunc, our Red Tops alert column, that journalist Edward 'Teddy' Beresford had been linked romantically with Julia Yates, the mercurial and, some might say, loopy wife of architect Anthony Yates.

Beresford was the exciting young prospect who blew up in the Hexroyd Tennis Club Under 18s' final, against the less talented but tough-as-teak Tom Hogg, in one of the most tense sporting fixtures I have ever covered. Undefeated all season against his contemporaries, Beresford looked nervous and unconvincing even before umpire Colin Sangster's controversial decision on match point.

Instead of rolling up his sleeves and showing his superior class, Beresford simply folded. He lost both the match and his reputation as a sportsman. He never recovered his poise on the tennis court, and he never recovered from the loss of his first love. It's common knowledge that Beresford had been making Hamlet look like Action Man as he dithered for ages over Rachel Waterfall. Friends say he had decided to make his move at that evening's club ball, the newly-crowned champion asking for the first dance with the club's loveliest member.

Beresford never showed that evening. Tom Hogg moved in for his second victory of the day and has ever since worn the look of a man who thinks someone up there must like him.

A few years ago, Beresford went to a cognitive behavioural therapist. She asked him if he felt that somehow he didn't deserve to be successful or happy. It might account for his lack of ambition. It might also enable us to explain the increasingly unsatisfactory nature of his relationships with women down the years. Those girls chosen purely for their looks, or the newly divorced seeking a quick fling after a messy settlement; and finally, now, a beautiful but unstable married woman who probably wants more from the relationship than he is prepared to give.

Meanwhile, Tom Waterfall, as he now calls himself, is an acclaimed television producer and film-maker who continues to prosper in life and in love.

History is written by the winners. Ask Waterfall, Ask West Germany's footballers. And ask Edward 'Teddy' Beresford.

CULL VALLEY EVENING GAZETTE

Saturday August 1 2009

The jewel in Yorkshire's crown

Teddy Beresford finds the historic city of York as delightful as ever

I never tire of York, the North's – and perhaps England's – finest small city. In 1984, I went for the first time on a primary school outing, and I've been a regular visitor ever since.

A glorious sunny day provided the perfect conditions for touring the historic city, and an orientation walk is a good way to start. It takes about an hour and a quarter to do a circuit of the medieval walls although, if you've only got time for one section, the ten-minute stretch from Monk Gate to Bootham Bar, with magnificent views of the Minster, is the one to go for. Nearby, on High Petergate, are some fine-looking pubs, one of which serves beers brewed within those city walls.

Regular visitors will have their own must-see places, whether it's the National Railway Museum, an exciting examination of rail history with a fabulous range of 'locos' to admire, the Minster (largest medieval church north of the Alps) or the Castle Museum, with its Victorian cobbled street full of shops.

But don't run away with the impression that York is merely a tourist honey trap set in some heritage time-warp. The modern shopper is well catered for at such developments as McArthur Glen and Monks Cross, on the city's outskirts. And there's a terrific range of High Street names, as well as plenty of smaller ones with which you will be less familiar. The same is true of the city centre itself, where independent traders, especially for women's fashions, are well represented.

An open top bus trip is another excellent way to get a feel for the city's layout. York is increasingly cosmopolitan and attracts students and tourists from around the world. Our bus was like a League of Nations, with passengers speaking German, Russian and Japanese. Just before we departed, we were joined by a young couple from Morocco – they had the national flag on their rucksacks, and a picture of John Lennon. They sat in front of us and chatted in Arabic, in a highly animated fashion.

If you're not on a tight budget, lunch in Betty's (or the nearby Little Betty's in Stonegate) is a must. For visitors with children, the Jorvik Centre is great fun, an opportunity to travel back in time 1,000 years, and learn some surprising facts about the Vikings.

The beauty of York's architecture never fails to impress and there are any number of hidden gems. Behind the Minster and next to quaint Chapter House Street, the elegant Treasurer's House can be found. It was originally the home of the treasurer of York Minster, and was restored to its former glory by a Yorkshire industrialist in the 19th century. Equally impressive is Fairfax House, the last word in Georgian interiors and furnishing.

And I haven't even mentioned York's guild halls – the Merchant Adventurers built in the 14th century is the most impressive. With so much on offer it would be easy to overlook the excellent City Art Gallery, which features 600 years of European painting.

York's got something for everyone. You'll be back, because on a day trip you can scarcely scratch the surface.

Letters to the Editor (Tuesday August 4)
Did Teddy Beresford actually visit York (The jewel in Yorkshire's crown, August 1) or was his priceless prose taken from a guide book? He certainly didn't tell me anything I didn't know, other than that he's well up on flags. Perhaps he had the Observer's Book as a kid. And it's nice to see that he recognises a good retail opportunity for the ladies when he sees one!

A Smithson
Smithson's Carpets
Mytholm Beck
Ainsley

STORIES...TEDDY....

The first time I was offered a foreign press jaunt, a night in Antwerp by ferry from Hull, I was nervous. I was still a new boy at the Evening Gazette and the trip had only fallen into my lap because several more experienced reporters wouldn't, or weren't allowed to, go without their partners.

"Suppose I don't see anything striking. Suppose nothing much happens," I said to Stan Cartwright.

"There's always something to write about, always something going on," he said. "Observe. Listen. Give me, your reader, a real feel for the place. I want your words to take me there."

I acquitted myself tolerably well in Antwerp, and a few other European cities, but my leaden prose didn't magically transport any readers to olde York's cobbled streets; the only person with me in any sense at all was Julia, who fancied a shopping expedition.

Our chief sub-editor, Frances 'Doc' Jekyll, also handles the letters page, an unenviable task, and one shaped to a considerable degree by the often desperate search for printable material. I've lost count of the number of times she's included letters taking issue with Gazette writers. Complaints that our reviews of amateur dramatics have an inadequate fulsome factor, now they're great favourites of the reader.

I'm not grumbling about A Smithson's views. He (or she, letter writers are often coy about gender) was on the money. But I thought that it was badly judged to print them.

I caught up with Jekyll, a rotund, heavy smoker whose face had been ravaged by three decades on 30 fags a day, in the staff kitchen. She was staring out of the window at the scurrying clouds, and toying with her packet of Marlborough, as if weighing the need for her fix against exposure to the elements.

"Fran," I said, eschewing as I always did her nickname, "It wasn't a colourful piece of travel writing, well, at least no more than beige. I'll hold my hands up, not my finest hour. But I'm not sure what purpose is served by printing the letter. Is this a trend? Cull Valley carpet sellers doing lit crits on Gazette reporters. Letters taking issue not because our facts are wrong, but because our prose is inelegant?"

"Don't be ridiculous," she said aggressively, a clear indication with Jekyll that she knew she was in the wrong.

"I'm not entirely convinced that McClair would be too pleased."

"Why would that be?" she said. I could see that, for a moment or two, she looked discomfited.

"Well," I said, "It points to the lack of sophistication at the Gazette, that we should have published such a dull piece."

"It was a reader's opinion, sometimes they like our stuff, sometimes they don't," she said.

I could see this wasn't going to get me anywhere.

My attempts to explain to Julia that I was writing a colour piece about a day trip to York had made no impression. "You've seen it all before," she said. Monks Cross and McArthur Glen did indeed provide splendid retail opportunities but they left too little time elsewhere. I managed half an hour in the Minster while Julia went to Monsoon. I loved the semaphore saints at the end of the nave, 12 headless figures holding haloes and signalling the message 'Christ is here'. As I examined them, a choir and a handful of musicians started practising a cantata, possibly Bach. It didn't stir me in any spiritual sense, any more than the day I walked into Santiago's cathedral and saw the swinging of the censer, but it was a beautiful moment for all that, and something I should have written about, rather than some daft personal stuff which infuriated the sub-editors. Later, Julia and I galloped down lunch in Betty's, but the alehouses proved no-go areas.

"You can go in pubs anywhere," she said.

"And you can shop anywhere," I should have replied.

I must sound like a wuss, but I was walking on egg shells after exhausting all my reserves of bravery during the open-top bus trip.

By one of those pointless coincidences that some people invest with great significance, Gill Swallow, the Gazette's veteran court reporter, was on the same bus as we were. I didn't think she saw us as we walked down the aisle, because she was preoccupied with her grand-daughter. We were followed by two young Moroccans who sat down next to Gill and the kid. This couple were so loved up and engrossed in each others' company that I felt a pang of jealousy.

"I think we'd better get off, Courtney-Paige," said Gill.

"Aw, Nanna, it's a nice view from 'ere," said Courtney-Paige.

"I'll get you a lolly instead."

Gill Swallow dragged Courtney-Paige to the stairs, doing a think-she's-going-to-throw-up mime for the benefit of the other passengers, while I hid behind one of Julia's shopping bags.

"What was that all about then?" I said to Julia.

"She must be worried about Al-Qaeda," Julia said.

"Al-Qaeda?" I said, implying sheer bewilderment, although I had an uncomfortable idea of where the conversation was heading.

"It's perfectly understandable. She thinks that they might have a bomb in their bag. We should get off, too."

"Bollocks, they are not Al-Qaeda, they are students from Fez," I improvised. "They are doing English as a foreign language in York. They visited Liverpool because they are great Beatles' fans. He likes Lennon; she prefers McCartney, and they both agree that George Harrison was never given due credit for his work. Both sets of parents are educated people who travelled widely before settling down to raise a family. They have been especially keen to ensure that their daughters have the same opportunities as their sons. Both generations are practising Muslims, but religion does not play a hugely significant part in their lives, and they have a great respect for other faiths, including Christianity and Judaism. So, no, I am not getting off the bus, but if you want to have a word with the driver, please go ahead."

"What?"

"Go on. Tell the driver that there are two terrorists on the bus."

"And just how embarrassing would that be?" she said.

"Less of a problem than being blown up, I'd say. We've got two options here. We tell the driver, or we stay put. What we don't do, under any circumstances, is walk away, while the bus and everyone on board is blown into 100 pieces."

"It's hardly likely to be as bad as that."

"While half the bus is blown up and everyone ends up in only 25 pieces."

"I'm getting off."

"Go on, then."

"You're going to make me get off on my own?"

"Yes."

She stayed put, but I was shaking like a leaf. I could feel the bad vibes coming off her. I knew that Julia would now feel that I owed her.

I was also aware that we'd gone well beyond the end of the line in our relationship, and that I should have acted already.

And now I knew that everyone in the office was talking about our affair, including Frances Jekyll. After I'd given up on the A Smithson letter, she was about to walk away when she discovered a new line of attack.

"We all know that you're shafting the architect's floozy. You're not the first, and you won't be the last. But the bottom line is this: your work's been going down the slot recently. That piece was poor, well below what you're capable of even though you've had a whole week to think about it, and you've not had your mind on your regular job recently. What was all that crap about going to York with your French pen friend and being too hung over to enjoy the trip? Readers don't want to hear that shit. We had to slice that one out."

"Yes, you were probably right there, Fran."

"And we all know that you took the Yates woman to York."

"How do you work that out then?" I said, stupidly; it was unlikely to be a stab in the dark by Fran.

"Gill Swallow spotted you behind all your tart's shopping bags. You're behaving in a totally unprofessional way."

"Not like Thrower then, the consummate pro."

"Don't you dare bring Ken into it. I know he likes the ladies, and okay he might have had the odd dalliance in the past, but he would never dream of letting his romantic entanglements get in his way at work. You're going to have to shape up damn quick, pal."

That was telling me, no one's accused me of being unprofessional before. I'd nothing to offer in return. Jekyll smirked as she headed for the staircase and staff exit, her desire for nicotine having won out.

The Yates ditching process had to begin, in earnest now, no more shilly-shallying. Julia would be my ex by the end of the month. Yes, we can put an actual date on this one. When I return after the August Bank Holiday, I am definitely going to be a free man, though not for too long I hope.

Who knows, I might even chance my arm with Sally Merrens, if she gets the job she's applied for at Hexroyd General Hospital. She did look rather fetching in the picture that accompanied her speed-dating feature earlier this year.

Would she still give me a chance after I blotted my copybook in January? Only one way to find out.

The National Diary

August 2009

A voice from the pulpit

'I had fulfilled my husbandly duty to God'

Anthony Yates, warden and lay preacher of St Luke's Church, Hexroyd, West Yorkshire, reflects on the sanctity of marriage, his first night as a married man and the responsibilities that come with matrimony

I always look forward to catching up with Jeannie Derby and the other church wardens at the vicarage, during the get-togethers which we hold once a fortnight.

There will, we hope, be time for talking about Jesus at some juncture during the afternoon, and about how He would react to the trials and challenges of our daily lives. Before that, however, there are practicalities to be considered; it never ceases to amaze me that some quite important issues inevitably arise in the run-up to our meetings. If a week is a long time in politics, it's an even longer stretch in the life of St Luke's!

It's a crying shame that the wife of Gerald, our vicar, doesn't provide more assistance for the flock. As occurred the previous week, it was Gerald who had to go off in search of the glasses, sherry bottle, and elderflower cordial for Jeannie, something that Marjorie might have been doing if she hadn't, once again, been at the hospital where she has a full-time job as a social worker.

Gerald had an important issue that he wanted to run past us. He gave us copies of the old 1662 Prayer Book because a few parishioners had requested a service, as they put it, "in the old style".

It was perhaps no coincidence that my copy opened at the Solemnization of Marriage, as this is something which has been very much in my thoughts of late. My eye fell on a section which read: "This Prayer next following shall be omitted, where the

Woman is past child-bearing" before continuing: "…that they may be fruitful in their procreation of children."

It served to remind me of my promises at my own wedding. Julia and I, together with other couples, attended some pre-wedding classes. Never was it suggested at any time that we had to keep on trying for babies. As far as I was concerned I had done my duty on the wedding night and, thinking hard about tight-trousered snooker players leaning over the table to reach the pink, twice more during the honeymoon. If Julia had failed to fall pregnant then, it was hardly my fault.

That first time had been the most disturbing. I didn't know where to begin and when Julia got into the bath I decided that I might as well join her. At least she would be clean. She plunged her face under the water and took my penis in her mouth. Somehow I managed to achieve an erection, maybe it was just the shock of the event. She licked me like a lollipop, came up for air and said in a little-girl voice: "Tony, fuck me. I'm ready now."

I didn't like to hear a lady talking like that and I knew that I wouldn't be able to stay hard for very long. So I decided that I had better perform straightaway. I managed to get it over with pretty quickly. "It'll be better next time," Julia said, unconvincingly. It wasn't, but at least we'd performed sexual intercourse three times by the end of the honeymoon.

My conscience was clear; I had fulfilled my husbandly duty to God.

Julia was, indeed, lucky that the marriage had been consummated at all, and that I had taken her on. I had been horrified to see the scars on her arm when she took off the 'going away' dress at the airport hotel. All the way up the inside of her left forearm was a series of white scars, some criss-crossed.

I asked about them, as gently as I could, and she replied: "I thought my mum had told you…that I tried to kill myself once." Eventually, I drew from her the information that she had self-harmed for six years, between the ages of 15 and 21.

I cursed her mother. No wonder she'd been so gushing when Julia first brought me to the house. She couldn't believe her luck in getting Julia fixed up with a 'catch' like me. If I'd known about this there was no way I would have got this far.

But, naturally enough, I was aware of the responsibilities that I had now taken on. And there were compensations. I had a pretty wife whose company I found perfectly tolerable, except when she had one of her mad turns. She would look after me in a practical way and we were able to take our place in society as a married couple, the way God intended.

We haven't taken it that step further by bringing a young life into the world but I am sure that must not have been God's intention.

It was my duty to care for Julia pastorally, and her duty to care for me practically. We have both found the way to fulfil those duties Our Lord had prepared for us on this Earth.

Julia's Journal

July 26, 2009: Teddy's selfishness knows no bounds. His trip to York was all about Me, Me, Me. "I've got to do this," "I've got to do that". Everyone knows what York Minster looks like. What precious insights can Teddy bring to bear by wasting his time in there? It's not as if he even believes in God.

But the worst of the day was on the bus tour of the town, hardly my idea of fun to begin with. Especially when you're shivering on the top deck and you're surrounded by kiddies screaming at the passers-by. One youngster was hauled off the bus by her grandmother who tried to give the impression that the brat was going to be sick. That charade didn't fool me for a moment. The nanna was as worried as I was about the Arabs sitting there cool as you like with their substantial rucksacks. Like in the Middle East, a tourist bus is just the place for a Jihadist with a bomb, and this pair looked very suspicious. Heads together with a real air of the conspiratorial about them. The last thing I wanted to do was draw attention to myself, but I thought it was key to follow the sensible nanna's example and get off. Teddy did not agree and told me what a model couple the Arabs were because they'd been to Liverpool and loved The Beatles. Personally, I can't stand The Beatles but whether you like them or not I don't see it proves anything. That could be a cover to make them look like us.

But that is only the half of it. The really, really upsetting business here was that Teddy proved such a coward. When he finished delivering his Beatles speech he was shaking like a leaf. In other words, he was even more scared than me and the old woman; he just wasn't prepared to do anything about it. If Teddy had clocked the look of fear on the nanna's face as she dragged poor little Paige, or whatever she was called, down the bus, that might have provided the jolt he needed. But, no, he was too busy rummaging around with the contents of one of my shopping bags to take in the enormity of what was going on around him.

Doctor gives me an 'eadhache!

Wednesday August 12, 2009

Middle-aged fogey Kenneth 'Chuck' Thrower takes a light-hearted look at the way we live today, as he explains why the eighth letter of the alphabet makes him see red. But he finds the company at the Mid-Pennine Chamber of Commerce dinner very much to his liking

There are aitch people and there are haitch people.

Haitches have always driven me to distraction. At one time you could put their use down to a lack of education, but the population of Haitchland is growing fast. One friend of mine, the boss of a small company, has suddenly started haitching in his 50s. The other week, I interviewed a haitching doctor.

In Vancouver I met a British man who had strong views on the immigrants from the Far East. "Let's hope they don't mess it up like they've done in Hong Kong," he said.

Well, a bit hard on the Chinese but only time will tell on that one, I reflected before he set my teeth on edge by saying that he had a job with HaitchSBC. Why, I wondered, was this goon lucky enough to work in one of the world's most beautiful cities, for an organization whose name he couldn't even say correctly? And why isn't HSBC's first instruction to new recruits: 'This is how we pronounce our name…?'

It's just another symptom of dumbing-down Britain. It might be a while before we get the first haitching cabinet minister but, in an era when senior politicians are more likely to admire Morrissey and Oasis than Mozart and Beethoven, don't expect to wait too long.

What would George Orwell have made of this? He suggested that the middle classes had nothing to fear from sinking into the working classes "but the loss of our aitches".

How wrong can a man be? The middle classes continue to expand, and many of us are gaining our haitches.

It's always a pleasure to attend the Mid-Pennine Chamber of Commerce dinner. This week I had the good fortune to get in conversation with the new chairman, Anthony Yates, and his delightful wife, Julia. Surprisingly, it was my first meeting with Anthony, one of the Cull Valley's most distinguished residents, although *Gazette* readers might recall that it was Julia who allowed me to 'test drive' her impeccably maintained 1966 Ford Anglia shortly before Christmas last year.

Julia, coincidentally, told me that she had known the Chamber's guest speaker, folk singer and entrepreneur Jeffrey Woodworth, when they were both students at Hereford University. "Even then, you could tell he was going places," said Julia, or words to that effect.

Woodworth, a regular guest speaker at business lunches and conferences talked about how he combined his entrepreneurial and musical activities. He also gave a funny and self-deprecatory account of his experiences as a young folk musician. His disastrous debut performance was typical of his inability to impress the ladies. A theatrical pause followed before someone, inevitably, said: "Was that you know who?"

"No, that was later," he said.

"Tell us who it was, Jeffrey, your secret's safe with us," a couple of wags shouted.

Well, most people do know Jeffrey because of *Tory Lady in Red*, his surprise hit single from a few years ago, although the identity of the crimson-clad female has never been revealed.

And Jeffrey certainly wasn't about to let it slip to guests at the Mid-Pennine Chamber of Commerce dinner!

STORIES...KENNETH....

"I see you've been to W Haitch Smith," Teddy quipped, pointing to my carrier bag as I came back into the office after lunch. Well, well, miracles do happen, the Beresford seal of approval for something I've written. Perhaps the intellectual snob was also impressed by my reference to Orwell.

When I discovered at the Chamber of Commerce 'do' that Julia Yates was a haitch person, I was tempted to say: "Is that haitch as in hadultery."

Needless to say I didn't, not least because I was trying to get on the right side of Anthony Yates. I should have recognized him on the day of the number-plate altercation, even though he was only the Chamber's deputy chairman at the time. I'm just relieved that Yates didn't remember me, although I'm surprised he hadn't known who I was. I am, when all's said and done, the second most senior journalist at the Cull Valley Gazette and I'm not embarrassed to say that the loss of status will be one of the hardest things to take on board when, a few years from now, it's time for me to bow out.

The column ended on an uninspired note, I thought. In the usual run of things I'm too much of a pro to make that mistake, but I'd done a last-minute piece of self-censorship. My final, rather punchier paragraph should have read: "Like the subject of that Carly Simon song (Warren Beatty, Mick Jagger?) we will probably never find out. Although someone, somewhere surely knows."

Because I've got my suspicions about this. Julia told me that she had met Woodworth at university. "He was a right smart Alec who knew he was going places," she said to me.

I did say that the reference to Tory Lady in Red went down well. But not everybody was laughing.

CULL VALLEY EVENING GAZETTE

Friday April 15 2005

Beresford's Beat

Losing my religion – Teddy Beresford describes a curious incident that had far-reaching repercussions

Is the world becoming a more dangerous place? There might be more crime but I'm not convinced that young people are at greater risk than they were when I was a child.

One Sunday morning, when I was nine-years-old, I set off to play in an important football match for the Cubs. I was stopped by a man with a short-back-and-sides haircut and a tidy little beard. He was called Peter and he'd just arrived in Ainsley. Peter wanted someone to show him round.

Mum and Dad had given me a special dispensation from church for the game but I was feeling guilty because I'd just passed my Sunday school teacher, Mrs Curbishley, in the street. Here was a chance to make amends to Mrs Curbishley. I thought about the way Jesus wanted us to help people in difficulty, but I had to play in my match first.

Peter sensed my indecision. "I can meet you here later," he said, and we agreed to that.

In the last minute of the match, I scored our equaliser.

"Oui! Formidable! Michel Platini does it again!" I said to my team mates.

But my joy was short-lived. There would now be five minutes' each way extra time, and I would have to keep my new friend waiting. To make matters worse, nobody scored, and we had to settle it with penalties. My educated right foot let me down; I shot wide with the crucial penalty because I was worrying about my map-reading appointment.

"How ironic that it should be you, after your exemplary performance, who missed the decisive spot kick, Edward," said Tom Hogg, our captain who liked to use fancy words.

I rushed to make my rendezvous but Peter never showed, or if he did he'd not waited long enough. I felt very bad; I had let everybody down.

We'd already learned at church about the Good Samaritan. The following Sunday, we heard a story about Jesus and Peter. That gave me an even worse conscience. I'd never until that point thought much about God, but now I decided that I'd been tested and must try harder.

I liked church, continued to go there long after my parents said I could drop it if I wanted to, and I even thought I might become a minister. I must have been 14 or 15 when some boys at school were talking about 'paedos' and the penny dropped.

I went straight to the vicar and told him that I wanted to give up my confirmation classes, as I no longer believed in God. I didn't mention Peter's accidental influence but I did ask whether non-believers could go to Heaven if they only found out when they died that they had been wrong after all.

"Because we don't have any choice about believing in God, do we?" I said. "You either think he exists or you don't. I've decided that he doesn't, and it's not my fault."

This is something I've given much thought to over the intervening years, and my fundamental view remains intact. You are wired for God or you aren't. If there is a God, he must have put the religious wiring in place, or – in my case – failed to install it. So I have total respect for people with faith (many of whom are far brighter than I am, intelligence is irrelevant) as long as they respect my right to be a non-believer. But the Rev saw things differently.

"No, Edward, I'm very sorry but that won't wash. Heaven, right now, would not be your destination. We must pray that you find your way back to us. At the day of reckoning, even as death beckons us, we will understand everything. All our mortal sins will be paraded before us. And, yea, we will learn how everything concerning us was seen and interpreted by the people we have known, loved and occasionally hurt because of our casual cruelty."

"Everything?"

"Everything, Edward."

I don't want to die before I get old. But I do want to know when the end is in sight. If my old vicar proves correct, the last few seconds of my three score and ten should prove very interesting.

TEDDY....

And that was the end of Beresford's Beat. The 'paedophile' column also brought my life as a news reporter to an abrupt conclusion.

It was not the only factor; I'd had a dodgy moment the previous month. A woman who had won a creative writing competition told me about her late husband's fight against cancer, then said she'd rather I didn't include it in my story. I stupidly mentioned this in passing to Thrower and he said: "No, this is too good to ignore. People will take inspiration."

"Yeah," I said, "But we've got to respect 'off the record' even if she didn't say it in so many words."

I was over-ruled, the cancer angle was reported, the widow went ballistic and Thrower somehow managed to distance himself from McClair's dressing-down.

When 'paedo' appeared, two local church ministers were incandescent and demanded some disciplinary action against me.

"You're becoming a loose cannon. We're putting you on the sub-editors' desk, under the supervision of Frances Jekyll. It might teach you some self discipline."

I imagine that this move was presented to the churchmen as relegation ("he won't be writing news stories or opinions any more, only the occasional feature in his own time") though technically it wasn't – subbing is a different job rather than 'better' or 'worse' – and for some it is, in any case, a logical career progression to learn a new skill. I took to the job reasonably well, although I never got on with Frances Jekyll.

Incidentally, Jeannie Derby, my religious friend, didn't find the column offensive.

She said: "You're right about faith; your old vicar was a fool. With friends like him, the Church of England doesn't need enemies. For what it's worth, I think you've got a far better chance of getting through the Pearly Gates than some people I know at St Luke's."

Monday August 17 2009

A song for Jeffrey

The worlds of folk singing and business rarely collide. But for guest columnist Jeffrey Woodworth, they are a natural fit. Jeffrey, a recent speaker at the Mid-Pennine Chamber of Commerce, explains how he got started as a musician

A few years ago I supported Jethro Tull at a gig in Manchester. I was talking to Ian Anderson afterwards and I asked him how he managed to combine recording and concert work with his salmon farming.

He said that one activity relaxed him from the other, and this got me thinking about the possibility of finding some way to supplement my income. Folk musicians rarely make a fortune, even the bigger names can be found playing in pubs and other small venues.

To be honest, I was already better off than most of my peers. My poppy song *Tory Lady in Red* upset the traditionalists but was a best-selling single (no, I'm not about to reveal her identity). A Mercury Prize nomination the following year as the token folkie restored my artistic credibility.

My decision to start an online world-roots music business, which would supply both recordings and musical instruments, proved to be a sound one. My timing was good due to an upsurge of interest in world music. So, if you want to hear a Moroccan/hip-hop fusion from the original label in Marrakesh, or acquire an Indian tabla, Japanese shakuhachi or Persian kamancheh, I'm your man. The business is not as distant from my performing life as Ian's fish is from his, but it nevertheless involves using a different part of the brain, and I've never been afraid of hard work.

I'm in demand as a public speaker, not least due to a well-honed patter. A story about my first gig at Hereford University always goes down well. I had my eye on a pretty piano player with a student group called The Lamb's Kidney Band. She was sitting on the front row with a heavy duffel coat on her knee. "You can put it on stage if you like," I said gallantly. I then put down my guitar and launched into Nic Jones's *Penguin Eggs*, affecting a nonchalant air with both hands deep in my pockets, rather than cupping one to my ear. I lost my balance, couldn't retrieve my hands and made a perfect, 90-degree fall, no hint of knee-bend, like David Jason in *Only Fools and Horses*. My head landed on the Lamb's Kidney girl's coat, which is why I suffered no more than mild concussion. I retired hurt, but returned to the club the following week where I was introduced as the horizontal traditionalist. Alas, my Kidney girl never returned.

I tend to find that, at business-related events, people really want to know about the music, and how I got started. It astonishes me how many frustrated Claptons and Springsteens there are among the most sober-suited executives, accountants and lawyers.

I'd played guitar since I was in my early teens, though I only started performing before audiences when I went to Hereford. I was studying law – bit of parental pressure there – which I hated. Friday was folk club night in the Mappa Mundi Bar. In keeping with the democratic nature of our music, local amateurs were allowed to do a couple of numbers before the main act came on. My voice is not unlike my hero's, Nic Jones, and I made a minor name for myself by impersonating him. As I grew in confidence, I got a few compliments from the professionals who were topping the bill. I'd never risked my own songs on an audience, but after Kathryn Tickell asked me if I'd written anything I started slipping the occasional home-grown number into my act.

It's been a case of hard work and some lucky breaks along the way. I sent a tape to John Peel and he gave me a few plugs – he liked my similarity to Nic, who had featured on *Top Gear* (for younger readers that was a Sunday afternoon programme on Radio 1, nothing to do with Jeremy Clarkson) in the late 1960s.

As for *Tory Lady in Red*, it's no more typical of my work than *My Ding-a-Ling* was of Chuck Berry's. The folk world seems to have forgiven me now, and the royalties were good; it certainly helped me to get a foot on the property ladder and to get my business up and running!

Stories they cannot print

JEFFREY WOODWORTH....

She was one of the oddest girls I ever met, and the inspiration for my hit song.

The first time our paths crossed was at the folk club. She was called Julia, and she was always there, singing along when one of the performers did something with a join-in chorus. She was a bonny lass and every Friday, during my Nic Jones tribute, I would give her my most winning smile as I sang Penguin Eggs, Miles Weatherhill or The Lakes of Shilin. Feeling particularly brave one evening, I winked at her during The Wanton Seed.

I followed that up by approaching her during the interval. Julia said something about folk being the music of the working man, which made me laugh because my dad was a top QC with an entry in Who's Who. I didn't tell her this, she didn't strike me as someone who would see the funny side of anything. She appeared to be a folk music groupie – a phenomenon, incidentally, that I'd never come across before and regrettably have never met since – and was only interested in that night's big name, Kev Heppenstall. Julia would buy the latest CD by the headline act and, from time to time, would leave with him. I do know that Kev hit the jackpot that night.

After a couple of terms, she stopped coming to the gigs. I still saw her on the campus, and said hello to her but she wouldn't pause to talk, so I never found out why she lost interest.

A few years later, round about the time my first album was released, I came across Julia again in Leeds city centre. It was shortly before a general election. She was campaigning on behalf of the Conservative candidate, a dashing young man, and she tried to give me a leaflet. I was playing at the Irish Centre that evening. I was a pro by now, and I remember thinking that if I'd had that status in my Hereford days I might have qualified for a one-night stand with Julia.

I knew she wouldn't remember me, but I told her who I was and what I was doing there. She continued to try to press the claims of this bloody Tory and I said: "Blimey, love, I don't think that you'll find many folk singers voting for that lot. It is," I added, remembering our first conversation, "the music of the working man."

"I don't go for that hand-in-the-ear, love-sick sailor stuff," she said, revealing that she had performed both musical and political u-turns.

My third meeting was the other week, at Mid-Pennine Chamber of Commerce. Anthony Yates, the newly elected chairman of the organisation, introduced me to the audience. Bugger me; if sitting next to him and done up to the nines, it wasn't his glamorous wife, Julia.

She told Anthony that we'd been pals at Hereford University, which raised the eyebrows of an ear-wigging hack from the local rag, called Thrower. It had the same effect on mine, too, as she'd barely condescended to know me from Adam in those far-off days of gigs in the Mappa Mundi Bar.

What, I wondered, would be Julia's current obsession? It wasn't long before I found out.

"I've had to give the gym a miss tonight, they'll be wondering where I've got to," she said.

"You're a regular there, I take it?"

"Three or four evenings a week and twice at weekends," she said.

"You look very trim," I said, as I could see that she was fishing for compliments. Not at all like our Hereford days when she was, if anything, a pound or two overweight (nothing wrong with that, I've never gone for skinny lasses), was one of the few students with a car, and never walked anywhere if she could use her wheels.

Her left-leaning days might be behind her, but she's still capable of Stalinist re-writes of history. I wonder what her next u-turn will be, and where will it take her?

229

CULL VALLEY EVENING GAZETTE

Monday August 24 2009

Reds find more questions than answers

A recent survey by the Licensed Victuallers' Association revealed that the Cull Valley is the nation's number-one spot for pub quizzes. Our resident know-all, Stan Cartwright, reports on the fortunes of his own team, the enigmatically-named Deirdre's New Cupboard, and explains the appeal of quiz nights

There was one round to go at the White Cutter Inn, Ainsley, and we Cupboard boys were level pegging with the Bean Counters.

Yes, you can tell quite a lot about folk by the names they give to their quiz teams, sometimes more than you need to know.

Bean Counters are local accountants, Everybody Do This are primary school teachers, and Come On You Reds are Manchester United supporters. It will be no great revelation for our readers to learn that this unimaginative group of individuals occupied bottom spot as we went into the final round, five adrift of Bond…Unibond, the team composed of Ainsley Athletic fans. As this is a family newspaper, I am not in a position to divulge the name chosen by the medical secretaries' side.

Last Wednesday it was cup night. Kicking off throughout the Cull Valley at 9pm, almost 200 quiz teams were asked exactly the same bunch of questions. The winner at each of the 32 pubs went through to the next stage of the competition.

Quiz sides, the medical secretaries notwithstanding, tend to be male dominated. Deirdre's New Cupboard comprises four chaps who have been "quizzing together" for many years, as a few keen soap opera fans might have guessed.

Our captain, librarian Bob Buckley, and I, together with Col Keegan and Nige Gibbs, reckon to have taken part in more than 300 pub quizzes in that time, with the odd ringer brought in to cover for illness or holidays.

People often ask if we spend our spare time learning facts, such as longest rivers, St Leger winners and capitals of countries. I can't speak for the others but, for me, that sort of thing isn't in the spirit of quizzing. There's no harm in dipping into *Schott's Original*

Miscellany, but that hasn't got anything to do with proper general knowledge.

Over the years we've won ourselves plenty of pints, as free beer is usually the main prize awarded to winners. I prefer it that way, to be honest. We've picked up a few bob, too – once we shared £80 from a weekly accumulator. But if money's involved, that's when mobile phone calls from pub lavatories spoil the spirit of the thing. At the end of the day, it should be all about enjoying the crack and downing a few decent pints.

All the team have got their particular areas of expertise, and we always hope that they will be well represented in the questions. Until the penultimate round, things fell very nicely for us on Wednesday, with current affairs which we're all big on, football and literature for Bob and me, rock music and science for Nige, and geography and travel for Col. Then we got stuck on a round about cars. That's not our forte, and the only point was scored by my knowing the make of vehicle in which Harry Potter is driven to Hogwarts.

But worse was to follow...

"Ladies and gentle-men," said landlord and quizmaster Jack da Silva. "Our final round of questions this week is on Reality TV."

There were groans all round from us. The Bean Counters, however, were pleased as Punch. And 15 minutes later, they were the team who were looking forward to moving into the next round of the competition.

Our Quiz Cup dreams were over for another season. For us, for Bond...Unibond, for the medical secretaries and all the other quizzers, there's always next year...and the chance in the meantime to concentrate on the Quiz League.

STORIES...STAN...

Before we started, Jack da Silva asked Captain Bob Buckley to explain the origins of our unusual name.

"It's from Coronation Street. The week we got together, a chap had come to fit a new cupboard in Deirdre Barlow's kitchen," said Bob.

"When was that?"

"Let's see now. It would have been long after her affair with Mike Baldwin, and closer to the time when the bloke who sold ties at Manchester Airport told her that he was a pilot."

"I'll settle for a year," said Jack.

"Late 1991, or early 92, I think it would have been."

I've spent the best part of two decades answering daft questions in a pub. My wife, Suzanne, thinks those quiz nights are sad, like most aspects of my life, from my role at the Gazette to my lifelong devotion to Ainsley Athletic.

"Why can't you support Park Avenue, Leeds or Manchester, like everyone else round here?" she says.

When I return from a quiz night, she takes great delight in asking me if we won, and "which of the Cupboarders played well".

"We all had blinders," I told her, the night we were knocked out of the cup by Bean Counters. "But what can you do when the deciding round is about Big Brother and the other ones?"

"It's a pity they didn't have any questions about Teddy Beresford," said Suzanne unsympathetically. "You'd have been all right there."

That is true enough, I do know all there is to know on the subject of Teddy. Give him a couple of pints of Golden Accelerator and his past tumbles out. Sometimes he doesn't even know that he's doing it, especially when he appears to be confusing his fantasies with the real world.

On one occasion, Teddy filled in for our pub quiz team because Col Keegan had flu. A question about tennis came up: 'Who won the Wimbledon men's singles title in 1986?' Teddy said: "I did," then added quickly, "I mean, yes, I did see that final, I'd have been 11 at the time. It was Boris Becker's second win, against Ivan Lendl." No one else batted an eyelid but I'll swear I saw him blush, and I'm fairly certain that he spotted me doing so.

But usually it's a simple case of in vino veritas, with Teddy telling me more about the nitty-gritty of his romantic entanglements than I need to know.

I can just picture the look of despair on the Bean Counters' faces when Jack da Silva announces that the night's questions will finish with "The Sex Life of Teddy Beresford"...

"First question," Jack might say: "What position is favoured by Julia Yates in her love-making sessions with Teddy."

"On top," I write, a question which, frankly, is insultingly simple.

"Two. How many women had Teddy Beresford slept with before he met Julia?"

"Twelve," I assert confidently.

"Of those women – your third question now – how many were single couplings, including one-night stands?"

"Two," I tell Bob, Col and Nige.

"Question number four. What word did a prostitute use to attract Teddy's attention as he walked down a back street in Las Palmas?"

Things are getting tougher now, and the Bean Counters are nervous. Col is embarrassed because, as the expert on geography and travel, he feels he should know anything connected with the Canary Isles. But I'm on the case.

"Rubio."

"Number five. How did Anthony Yates get the absolute confirmation that his wife was having an affair with Teddy?"

"He came home early from work, and found semen on the sheets."

"Six. What unusual injury occurred to Beresford, when he made love to Julia Yates last weekend? Here's a clue for you: it was al fresco."

"Stung by a nettle."

"Finally, question seven. How does Teddy Beresford avoid premature ejaculation when Julia's passionate love-making becomes almost too hot to handle?"

This is the killer question. Looking across the room, from Come On You Reds to the medical secretaries team, We Can Spell Colpoperineorrhaphy, there's a wailing and gnashing of teeth. Bob, Col and Nige look to me for inspiration. I scratch my head and look at them blankly.

"Only kidding, lads," I say, before writing: "He imagines the most boring thing possible, a snooker player getting a 147 break."

I try not to look too smug. It's in the bag for Deirdre's New Cupboard.

Advertisement Feature

(Draft copy, FAO Teddy Beresford)

Summer Magic

Heavy rain failed to dampen the spirits at the Cull Valley Agricultural Show, and now it seems that an Indian summer beckons.

Forecasters say that we should be in for some glorious weather throughout the last few days of August and early September. The long, warm evenings are going to be with us with any luck until the schools go back, so there will be plenty of opportunities for getting out and about, and discovering the delights of our neighbourhood.

As Shakespeare observed, "summer's lease hath all too short a date". So make hay while the sun shines.

Here in the Cull Valley, there's no shortage of glorious countryside, stately homes and wonderful places to eat and drink.

There are also some superb and unspoilt public houses, many selling real ale from Yorkshire microbreweries. These include local favourite Cockcroft's, which was established just ten years ago by Hexroyd microbrewer Timothy Cockcroft. Tim has become a regular prize winner at beer festivals throughout the country, notably for his IPA and Golden Accelerator ales.

Real ale is far more widely available than it was a generation ago and pubs have changed too, often serving food of restaurant standard, with meat sourced locally from the likes of butchers Eric and Paul Hopkinson. The days when you could walk into a pub at lunchtime with your packed lunch, say to the landlady: "Can I eat in here?" and get the reply: "Yes, I'll give you a plate," have long gone.

By the same token, many restaurants now serve good beer. But Apfelbaum, run by Garry and Ursula ('Uschi') Ellison, is unusual in having a draught bitter alongside some fine bottled beers, and an excellent wine list. Hand-pumped Accelerator is always on tap, and always on top form, too. The Hexroyd and Ainsley branch of CAMRA recently gave Garry's beer an honourable mention in its monthly magazine, *Valley Tipplers*.

Incidentally, Tim Cockcroft named his best-selling ale as a tribute to his namesake and hero Sir John Cockcroft of Todmorden, Lancashire, Nobel Prize winner and co-builder of the world's first proton accelerator.

There's no need to join the traffic jams this weekend. Stay local and enjoy some terrific food and drink on the doorstep.

From: Edward.beresford@univalleypapers.co.uk
Date: 14 August, 2009 14:27
To: Stanley.cartwright@univalleypapers.co.uk
Subj: Brewer's scoop

I was delighted to see the reference to Sir John Cockcroft in your out-and-about feature (Summer Magic). This modest and kindly man was one of the greatest British scientists of the 20th century. In this age of obsession with fame for its own sake, celebrating the work of such a great man is utterly refreshing. Like the beer! Well done, Timothy Cockcroft. And well done to the *Gazette* – it's nice to see you making amends for your nonsense about Sir Noel Armstrong!

No need for the red pen this time!

Yrs, Teddy

The National Diary

Country Diary

August 2009

Commas provide pause for reflection

By Park Ranger

The show season is in full swing right now, that wonderful time of year when town and country meet. All over England, people are coming together for business and pleasure, as well as to renew old acquaintances at fairs such as the Cull Valley Agricultural Show. This event, now well into its third century, returned to Ainsley last week.

For the first time since the show started in 1889, it went ahead a day late. Storms had left the showground waterlogged, but the tents and marquees lived to tell the tale. Paths were reinforced with duckboards and Astroturf so that spectators were able to keep their feet dry while horses and riders, cattle and sheep squelched their way through the mud to receive their rosettes.

The showground is on the edge of town, and fields lie beyond. There, the barley had already been gathered in before the weather changed, the grain safely stored and the straw saved, in the nick of time, for winter bedding.

The field edges are more exposed now and reveal the bramble in full bloom, attracting butterflies, such as commas, peacocks and red admirals, which for almost a week have been hiding in the woods for fear of drowning.

The presence of the comma (Polygonia c-album, easily identifiable by its ragged wings) is particularly fascinating to lepidopterists. Twenty years ago, you wouldn't have seen it much in the Cull Valley, comma territory being largely throughout Wales and the English counties south of a line running from Merseyside to Lincolnshire.

In fact, Yorkshire now hosts plenty of commas for the first time in almost 200 years, a result perhaps of global warming. In the 1820s, the butterfly was a familiar sight throughout the country but by the outbreak of World War One, as the Cull Valley Agricultural Show celebrated its Silver Jubilee, it had become very rare indeed.

The comma's existence is a fragile one, and the lighter females are pursued aggressively for mating purposes by the male, not unlike way the human world works. However, eagle-eyed naturalists might have spotted an inversion of this practice yesterday by two Homo sapiens in the more secluded woodland of the Cull Valley. There, the female, increasingly desperate to tackle the fading commitment of the male, forced herself upon him close to a path occasionally used by other humans. It was an aggressive coupling, one which the weak-willed male was powerless to resist despite the proximity of weedy plants of the temperate urticaceous genus.

Humans are a species who usually mate *in camera*, and this atypical behaviour is often associated with what its participants refer to as 'dogging': the male and female, previously unknown to one another, arrange via some technological channels, such as Blogs and Tweets, to come together. Less commonly, *al fresco* sexual activity indicates a breakdown in a long-standing relationship. The male or female might now choose to initiate intercourse close to others of their kind, with the consequent fear of discovery, to regain lost passion, some kind of 'spark', or perhaps because one participant is trying to indicate to the other half what he or she will be missing if the relationship is terminated.

This phenomenon has been observed in English literature, notably in *Sons and Lovers*; a couple go through a phase of fucking in the Nottinghamshire countryside shortly before they part company, and the female returns to her original partner.

As the happy crowds began to make their way home from yesterday's Cull Valley Show, some carrying trophies, rosettes and the home-baked fancies they had entered for competition, a doomed relationship was being consummated for the final time in nearby woodland.

The lucky naturalist who spots such an encounter is unlikely to hear much in the way of verbal exchanges between the parties, although on this occasion the male did, in a moment of post-coital frankness, say: "I have lost my job, and I think we need to do some talking about our future."

The National Diary

August 2009

A lawyer advises

Freddie Tilson, of Busby, Tilson and Bray, looks at your problems

Employment law is a field in which we have inevitably been very busy recently because of the economic downturn. Not all firms are playing fair in this climate, but many well-meaning employers are genuinely faced with a dilemma.

Do they do nothing, keeping everyone on board as turnover drops, while hoping that they might just turn the corner soon? Or do they make the sort of cuts, including shedding a few staff, which will at least give the company a fighting chance of surviving and ultimately thriving in the long run. It is possible that some bosses will use the recession as an excuse to downsize their operations, but others act in what they hope will be the best interests of the company.

Some redundancy decisions might seem perverse, targeting people who could have proved useful for growing the company in future, while apparently less worthy employees are spared. This would be of no concern to industrial tribunals, who aren't interested in whether a decision to make redundancies is sensible. Their only concern is whether it was done in a genuine and fair way. A tribunal will be reluctant to get involved in decisions made for business reasons and will need substantial evidence of underhand practice by a company. Take a look at the following.

Dear Mr Tilson – Until last week, I was employed as a journalist on the local newspaper. As a sub-editor, my role included reading and correcting editorial 'copy' to ensure, for example, that articles and stories had the right 'angle', read well, were grammatically correct, and fitted the page. In my case, these responsibilities usually included dealing with a light-hearted column written by the paper's deputy editor, Kenneth Thrower.

The company said that several redundancies would have to be made and I was informed that my job was at risk. Following a consultation period, it was announced that I would be one of four compulsory redundancies.

If I'd simply been told my job was redundant, as a result of re-organisation, I could have lived with it. However, the decision came down to a perverse scoring system in which my competency was judged by two senior editorial staff: yes, the very same Thrower, and my line manager, Frances 'Doc' Jekyll.

I believe that I was given unreasonably low scores simply because of some personal animus towards me on the part of Thrower and Jekyll. On more than one occasion, I've had to remove some injudicious comments from Thrower's column, and I have also been going out with a woman who rejected him in favour of me. I'll admit that I've never liked Frances Jekyll. There's some history between us which dates back to my time as a work experience student at the paper. But I thought she would assess my work fairly. She didn't and, allegedly without consultation, came to the same conclusion as Thrower.

So I ended up ranked as my department's worst performer and the company dispensed with my services. The markers colluded, no question. There's nothing in my staff file to suggest that I have performed badly, in fact what little evidence there is rather suggests the opposite. However nobody, including the union, thinks that I have leg to stand on.

Yours sincerely,
Edward Beresford

Dear Mr Beresford – Let's cut to the chase, shall we? I don't believe that you would have any chance of success at a tribunal. In a nutshell, where's the evidence?

To ensure fairness in selection for redundancy, an employer must establish that it has been done in a reasonable fashion, using objective criteria. I think the company could argue with some justification that it has done precisely that.

To summarise, as I see it, your dilemma: the company decided that one person had to go in your section. That was their decision, whether sensible or not. We could use a sporting analogy here. One football team will always have to finish bottom of the league, no matter how high the standard or how much they all spend on players. In the same way, someone in your department has to get the fewest marks. That person was you. It doesn't suggest that they thought you incompetent, merely that you weren't such a proficient operator as others in the 'squad'. Yes, there might be some truth in the observation that your staff file carries no written record of poor performance. But the same rules applied to your colleagues. The redundancy process appears to have been a level playing field.

That does not mean that you are without justification for your anger. It *is* most certainly unfortunate that there is no written record of any disagreement between you and Kenneth Thrower, regarding changes made to his column, for example. Had these existed, it might just have been possible to establish that you were acting wisely and professionally – for example if you removed a potentially racist viewpoint, and that Kenneth Thrower must therefore have been guided by malice in his assessment of you. I must admit that Thrower does sound like an unsavoury character, and that your female assessor sounds more like Mrs Hyde than Dr Jekyll. But it's simply their word against yours, which will cut no ice with a tribunal. In the same way, you suggest collusion between Jekyll and Thrower. But, again, there's no evidence of this.

It's also possible that you would have lost your job whoever had been doing the assessment. Even apparently nice people can turn nasty in such dog-eat-dog situations. Just be glad that you haven't been turned over by one of your friends.

As things stand, I don't see how you could expect to have a reasonable prospect of succeeding at a tribunal. It does sound as though you are going to have to take the redundancy package and leave gracefully. The union is probably right. I can't offer you anything more optimistic. Sorry.

CULL VALLEY EVENING GAZETTE

Advertisement Feature

Saturday August 29 2009

Out and about for the bank holiday

Another bank holiday is here, a time for getting out and about, and discovering the delights to be found further afield than your neighbourhood. Make the most of it, as this is the last break we'll see until Christmas. The days will soon be getting shorter.

Here in the Cull Valley, there's no shortage of glorious countryside, stately homes and wonderful places to eat and drink. But it's great to explore further afield.

So don't listen to those pessimists who put you off with talk of bank holiday traffic jams. If you set out good and early you can be well on your way to the destination before the rest of the world has got started.

Why not take a picnic with you? The forecast for the next few days remains good. Picnicking is a fun, old-fashioned idea and a good way of avoiding the pubs and restaurants that are likely to be excessively busy this weekend.

Or why not use the bank holiday to look for a new-to-you car? The area's second-hand salesmen have got together in a special initiative to promote their wares, and they will be open for all three days of the break.

Dealers will be happy to let you put a motor through its paces. Prices start at around the £1,000 mark but there are many second-hand cars which are less than a couple of years old. They still have that new car smell and they will cost you far less than a brand-new vehicle, as well as having any teething problems sorted out by someone else.

Have you got an ageing relative? There comes a time when independent living becomes impracticable and residential and nursing homes have the answer. The weekend could be an opportunity to look at a few lovely homes, and get a feel for whether any of them might be the place your senior loved ones would like to live in. A place, ideally, with a friendly, family atmosphere, lively calendar of social activities and gardens to enjoy during the summer

Whatever you are doing this weekend, have a great time.

STORIES...JEANNIE DERBY....

That loathsome man Kenneth Thrower has just pulled off a really below-the-belt trick on me.

"Could you do a big favour and give me 350 words on getting out and about, trying second-hand cars and looking at nursing homes?"

"Activities I do every Bank Holiday, when I'm not at prayer," I said.

Thrower laughed in that ghastly ingratiating way he has when he wants to butter you up.

"I really would be grateful, Jeannie. Stan's a bit under weather and he's had to go home."

"Okay, sure," I said, then rattled out 350 words precisely.

Had I known the real reason for Stan's departure, that he'd been shown the door along with Teddy, I would have told Thrower to put his fucking Out and About for the Bank Holiday where the sun doesn't shine, a threat that would have made him sit up good and proper as I only swear biennially.

Julia's Journal

August 30, 2009: With great sadness I have to report that this will be my last JJ. Things haven't worked out with Teddy. In fact, things haven't worked out with Anthony either, and things, if you really stop to think about it, haven't worked out for the best in any way, shape or form whatsoever.

Teddy says that it is all over between us.

He gave me the news over a pot of tea in a café near the charity shop. He told me there was something that he had to say and his hands were shaking. I could see that he was very nervous and, for a crazy second or two, I thought: "He's going to propose to you, Lady."

I was looking at a picture on the wall, the moment he said what he had to say. It was an old 1950s' railways poster, urging people to travel by train to Greenwood Crags.

Teddy had looked around very carefully at all the people in the café before he said anything. I think he was making sure that there was nobody we knew in case I created a scene. I was determined not to lose my dignity, and I gave the impression of being calm about the whole business.

He put his hand in mine and said: "You're being very understanding."

"It's alright," I said, "Now that you haven't got a job, it would very difficult for you to support us both."

He didn't know what to say to that.

"Is Ruth feeling better now?" I asked eventually, a time-filling sort of question while I tried to process all the information that was being thrown at me. "She was quite poorly the other night and I wondered what the problem might be."

"Ruth? Yes, she's fine. In fact if you asked her she would probably reckon never better," he said.

"Oh, she *is* pregnant, then?" I said, smiling broadly.

"I'm not so sure about that."

"Come, on Teddy, the secret's safe with me."

"Well, yes, as a matter of fact she is, but mum's the word for a few weeks."

The bitch. I thought as much when we were in Apfelbaum. I used to be sceptical about the idea that we girls had a sixth sense over other women's pregnancies. But I just fucking knew that Ruth was knocked up. Although the clues were there: the feeling below par, the avoiding alcohol, the concern expressed by both Rory and Teddy for her well being.

"You told me she'd been having difficulty conceiving. Did she decide to go for IVF in the end? They must be absolutely thrilled," I said through gritted teeth.

"Yes, they are."

"Wow, that's so exciting for them," I enthused. "It's all happened very quickly, hasn't it? Did they go through the usual channels?"

"Channels?"

"For sperm donation," I said.

"Who said anything about sperm donation."

"You said they were looking into it."

"Did I?"

"Of course you did," I said. He wasn't very comfortable with the turn this conversation was taking. "All I mean is, it's all happened very quickly. They weren't tempted to go through one of those unregulated donor websites, were they?"

"No, no I'm sure they wouldn't have risked anything like that," he said, scratching his nose nervously.

A ridiculous thought suddenly occurred to me, but the more I dwelled upon it, thinking back to Apfelbaum, the less crazy it seemed.

"You're the donor, aren't you, Teddy?" I said decisively, as if there were no doubt in my mind.

"Me?" he said, trying to look astonished but hesitating fatally.

"It's all right," I said. "I think that's a wonderful thing to do for someone you really care about. Don't worry, your secret's safe with me. One hundred and ten per cent safe."

"No, no, I don't understand how you can have picked up that idea for one moment," he said.

I was seconds away from doubting myself when he did his thumb on filtrum trick.

Right, Lady, I decided, time for a final assault on Mount Beresford.

"Teddy, you're such a sweet, sweet man. I know you're the sperm donor, it was so obvious from the way Ruth looked at you when you asked after her health. It's something you should be proud of, but I do understand that it is absolutely a private matter for the three of you. But it's quite upsetting that you're sitting here trying to deny it now, when I'm in such an emotional state. You know that I'd never, ever betray a confidence like that. Surely, after the last few, wonderful months together you've learned to trust me."

"Of course," he said, unconvincingly.

"Then isn't it just a teeny, weeny bit insulting to imply that I'm not to be trusted after all?"

"It's not exactly a matter of trust."

"Well, what is it? How much more do I have to spell it out? This goes no further."

I do believe I might have succeeded in shedding a tear at this point.

246

"Julia," he said after a long pause, "Yes it's me. But they really, really wouldn't want anyone to know about it. It's very private as you say, and it's very important indeed that nobody knows."

Mission accomplished. Flag planted on Mount Beresford. What to do next was the question.

"Teddy, Teddy, you're worrying yourself to death about nothing. No one will ever hear it from me. I can promise you that, my hand on my heart."

I almost felt sorry for him. Maybe he felt that his indiscretion added another layer of complete and utter finality to our relationship. Not only have I have lost my job, he was saying, but there can be absolutely no going back because I am a total shit who has betrayed you.

"I hope we can still be on friendly terms," he said.

"Of course, I'd like that, and I think that Anthony would too, now that the situation has been resolved."

"Anthony?" he said.

"Yes," I reassured him. "You know he likes you really, it's just been a difficult situation for him to cope with. It's been so tough for all of us."

"Yes, that's true enough. Tough for all of us," he repeated. "But perhaps we could all meet up, um, very soon."

Teddy bit his tongue, as if he'd made an unnecessary concession.

"How about tomorrow," I suggested, a plan forming itself in my head even as we spoke. "Now that Anthony's leg is out of plaster he's just itching to get out and about for the holiday."

"Er, fine," Teddy said. I could see that the idea of spending time with Anthony was not enticing, but he wasn't going to say anything that might spoil my conciliatory mood.

So we're meeting up on the final day of the bank holiday. Let's hope for nice weather, after the disappointingly wet days we've had recently, particularly in the run-up to the 121st Cull Valley Agricultural Show.

Here in the Cull Valley, as I'm often reading, there's no shortage of glorious countryside, stately homes and wonderful places to eat and drink. But it's great to explore further afield, too.

I think the best idea would be to drive somewhere, and take a picnic with us. The long-range forecast is fine, and don't you think that picnicking is a fun, old-fashioned idea?

As Teddy and I were about to say goodbye outside the café, I felt an overwhelming conviction about the rightness of the plan forming in my head. An act of pure and perfect revenge on Teddy, Anthony and the world.

Teddy was still rattling on obsequiously. "We'll be continuing to live close to one another." Blah blah. "A lot of water has gone under the bridge." Blah blah. "I dare say it's best for the three of us to be on good terms." Blah blah.

He smiled wryly as he said this, in that way he has when he thinks he's being witty.

"What's so funny?" I asked.

"I was just thinking of something that occurred to me once before, in a different context. You know, two men and a woman knocking about together, like *Jules and Jim*."

I have not the first fucking clue who Jules and Jim might be but I smiled anyway and said that I was looking forward to tomorrow.

Teddy might have betrayed me, but when I said his secret was 110 per cent safe with me, I was telling the truth. No one will ever, ever know.

Monday August 31 2009

A8814, West Yorkshire, 11-27am

"That's it, then," says Anthony, and I wonder cruelly if his faith has deserted him at the moment of reckoning.

"Goodbye, Reggie," says Julia.

Through the car window I see a farmer on a tractor, right hand above his eyes, as though he's saluting us. He will be our eyewitness in the *Evening Gazette*'s report tomorrow.

And what of my thoughts? Beatles albums, got to get them in chronological order. *Please Please Me*, the one that Philip Larkin mentions though not by name, *With The Beatles*, *A Hard Day's Night*, *Beatles for Sale* (bit disappointing that one, I always thought), *Help!*, *Rubber Soul*, *Revolver*, *Sergeant Pepper's Lonely Hearts Club Band*, *Magical Mystery Tour* if you count that one, only an EP but it came out as a long player in the States and I've got it in both versions, *Abbey Road*, no hang on a sec that's not right.....

In any case, there are a few things I've got to sort out in my head first, so they must take priority over the Fab Four. There are goodbyes to do...several pieces to sort out for the *National Diary* before the deadline. We've got a fabulous edition lined up for September 1.

There's a fascinating offering by a new member of the *National Diary* team, who has been signed from the *Cull Valley Evening Gazette*. I've put previous differences aside to bring her in, and I think you'll agree it was smart move. Then there is one familiar name: Ray Hutton from Ainsley Battling Cancer, a long-term *Diary* reader. I'm hoping – this might prove a big 'ask' but believe me I'm pulling out all the stops – to get a one-off contribution from Mark McClair, editor of the *Evening Gazette*.

Most importantly, as I bid the world farewell, I must supervise transfer of the *National Diary*'s editorship to a safe pair of hands. I know that Mark's disappointed not to have been under consideration and I trust that he will be a big enough man to take it on the chin.

What kind of a person are we looking for in the hot seat? Well, *The National Diary* is going to need someone who can build on our proud tradition while remaining very much his own man. Stan Cartwright is the obvious choice, but he's ruled himself out. His future plans do not feature journalism at all. Or Mrs Cartwright for that matter, but there's no time to go into that now. Maybe I need to widen the net, search for a maverick choice.

Incidentally, it has been brought to my attention that many of our readers have plenty of disposable income, are keen on travel and like to read about it. The new editor must be prepared to commission the very best people to bring foreign fields to life – to really "take you there". I've a few names in mind for him: they include Henry 'Hank' Hawley, who wants to fulfil a lifetime's ambition with a visit to Nashville, Tennessee, the home of country music. Butcher and *bon viveur* Paul 'Paolo' Hopkinson would be the perfect choice to explore the Eternal City before heading south to his Neapolitan mother's native Campania.

Yes, these are exciting times for the *National Diary*. There's a lot for me to sort out before I go, and I've never missed a deadline so I'd better crack on with my final edition.....

The National Diary

(Established in 1986)
September 1 2009

'Blame it on the little lady'

Julia Yates – villain or victim? Frances 'Doc' Jekyll, our new women's page editor, detects more than a whiff of misogyny running through press coverage of a triple death in Yorkshire

Everyone is now calling it the 'Harry Potter crash'; the appalling insensitivity of the tabloid press, who coined the term, is contagious.

For the benefit of those few people who have not followed the story, this was the accident on a West Yorkshire road in which housewife (as she has invariably been called) Julia Yates, the vehicle's driver, died together with her husband, Anthony, and local journalist, Teddy Beresford.

The tittle-tattle in local pubs has had a depressingly predictable misogynistic ring to it. (One landlord was even heard to say "That's lady drivers for you". In fact Julia Yates was an associate member of the Central Pennine Branch of the Institute of Advanced Motorists).

The coroner recorded a verdict of accidental death. That should surely have marked the end of all pointless speculation. Instead, rumours and counter-rumours abound regarding what really happened on that fateful bank holiday weekend. Some say that Julia and Teddy were having an affair, some declare that the hapless journalist was her latest in a long line of lovers, many observers suggest that Anthony Yates was gay, in which case he might well have been happy to turn a blind eye to many of his beautiful wife's affairs.

The one constant has been the suggestion that if there had been no affair, there would have been no accident. And that, in any event, Julia Yates was the villain of the piece: Julia Yates the gold digger who had settled for a loveless marriage in order to be a lady who lunches; Julia Yates the promiscuous woman who ensnared every remotely passable man who came into her path, whether it was an ageing Lothario from the same paper which until recently employed Teddy Beresford (what *is* her thing about hacks on local rags, I never saw much to tempt me in my days as a cub reporter covering country fairs in Lincolnshire?) or a hard-of-hearing 25-year-old charity shop worker; Julia Yates, the hard-as-nails bitch who said herself that she always got what she wanted, whether it was a new sports car, a holiday in the Seychelles, or (the one thing that finally eluded her) a baby.

Yes, boys, Julia Yates. Blame it on the little lady.

We are, I suppose, talking about the same Julia Yates ensnared into a lavender marriage by a self-righteous prig who craved respectability from polite society; the Julia Yates who did tireless charity work in shops such as Ainsley Battling Cancer; the Julia Yates who put any thought of a career on one side to support her husband; and the Julia Yates who finally wore her heart on her sleeve, and decided she would willingly forgo the trappings of life on Hexroyd's most affluent estate for the comparative austerity of a shared apartment in the former Barrowclough Mill with her low-earning lover.

Which Julia Yates is it to be? You pays your money and you takes your choice.

Except that you don't, do you? There's no bloody choice. Everyone, even to their undying shame most of the women I know, has swallowed the idea that Julia Yates was a black-hearted, self-centred narcissist who would stop at nothing to get her own way, destroying anyone who was foolish enough to stand in her path.

And who, in the end, has she destroyed? I think all the men, not least the egregious Beresford, who queued up for a bit of rough and tumble with someone out of their league should be bloody grateful that they got a look-in at all. If Julia disposed of them brutally at times, did they not stop to consider that she was only behaving in an utterly masculine way: having her fun then moving on?

For me, Julia Yates is the victim of this story. Victim and heroine, the one person to emerge with any credit. Not that you can expect to hear such an opinion expressed in any pubs, or through the columns of any newspapers other than the rare beacon of common sense and morality that the *National Diary* has now become.

As James Brown said: "This is a Man's World." And don't let anyone tell you anything different, Sisters.

Meet our readers

This week, the *National Diary* says hello to voluntary charity worker and retired woodwork teacher Ray Hutton, aged 67, of West Yorkshire. Ray has been a keen reader for more than 20 years

What do you like about the National Diary, Ray?
Where do I begin?! Its news coverage is comprehensive, it's great on sport, taking it seriously but with an occasional sardonic edge, and there are fascinating and quirky features.

Which Diary writers do you admire most?
I think that Jenny Dudley has a refreshingly upfront way of dealing with readers' problems, and Jon Stretford is a very good sports writer. I'll never forget that analysis of the Beresford psyche, prompted by Stretford's visit to Berlin and his recollections of that catastrophic Hexroyd Tennis Under 18s' final defeat. First-rate psychological insight.

It's truly remarkable the way the *Diary* continues to come up trumps, confounding our occasional fears about its editorial direction. I have to confess to deep consternation when I heard about the appointment of Frances 'Doc' Jekyll from the *Cull Valley Evening Gazette*. I'd always assumed that her communication skills were no more than three out of ten and that she could barely string a sentence together; I reckoned that she would be totally out of her depth at the *Diary*. So, credit where it's due. The retiring editor, Teddy Beresford, showed me her article before we went to press and I can see that she has got off to a cracking start with her absurd but well-argued feminist take on the A8814 Harry Potter tragedy.

However, at the end of the day, Henry Hawley has to be the main man for me. I was introduced to his writing through the *National Diary* and, needless to say, I was first in the queue at the local bookshop when both *Wingers and Whippets*, and *Quintessence of Dust* came out. I can't wait to see what he dreams up next!

Any changes you'd like to see in the Diary?
It's not a newspaper with much of a tradition for investigative journalism, is it? In my neck of the woods, the Cull Valley, I could

name several recent occurrences which would be worthy of much closer attention.

Give us an example

Well how about that Harry Potter car tragedy, *pace* 'Doc' Jekyll's splendid polemic? An acquaintance of mine who helped out in the Ainsley Battling Cancer (ABC) shop died recently in that crash. The coroner's verdict was accidental death, but the driver (another ABC assistant) was bonkers. If that was an accident, I'm a post-structuralist La Paz-based poet. No one has ever searched for the truth about that crash.

We'll see what we can do, Ray. Meanwhile, how have you been helping ABC?

Well, I'm involved with the property market – in a very small way, of course! My wife, Victoria, died of cancer shortly after I retired and I found that getting stuck into practical work, making dolls' houses, helped me through the saddest period of my life. I'd also started working a day a week in one of the charity's two shops. Naturally, the first two houses were made for my grand-daughters, Lucy and Alice. After that, it occurred to me that I could make more houses and sell them to raise funds for ABC. A couple of houses have been sold through ABC's Christmas raffles, and now word's getting round I've got a waiting list of people who would like to buy them.

It sounds terrific, Ray. Give us an idea of the detail that goes into building each house

Well, they're quite large, and made from wood (bought locally) as you can see from the picture of me with my most recently finished 'property'. There are three floors and eight rooms. It's decorated throughout so that will make life easy for any Borrowers moving in. But it's not furnished. They will have to find their own furniture! I'm now working on a big one, modelled on the Barrowclough Mill apartments. Oh, I also work in the ABC shop, where I met a friend of mine, Andy Dougan.

Didn't you have a rather tricky moment in the Mason's the other night when you were waiting for Andy to turn up?

Yes, I did and sad to say it involved Teddy Beresford, the acquaintance who died in that car crash that I was telling you about, you know, the one that warrants further investigation. He told me that he'd lost his job, and he said: "This must be the worst thing that's ever happened to me," or words to that effect.

I said, a trifle abruptly: "If that's as bad as it's got, you must have had an easy ride, Matey."

Well, I drank the last of my pint, banged down my glass rather too forcefully on the bar, and was about to give him a piece of my mind when Teddy apologised for his lack of tact. Obviously, I was upset because of my Victoria. Thankfully, Teddy and I parted on good terms. It was the last time I saw him.

Natural-born leaders

In our occasional column about leadership, we put the spotlight on Mark McClair, editor and managing director of the *Cull Valley Gazette* newspaper in West Yorkshire

You've been in the hot seat for many years, Mark. How do you see the editor's role – and how will it continue to evolve now that you've missed out on the National Diary job?

I see myself equally as a journalist and a leader. I like to think that I'm a good all-round journalist, and a great communicator of my vision for this wonderful paper of which I'm so proud. But as a leader, it's about empowerment of people. And that means putting your trust in the right individuals. To be able to do that you've got to know what's going on at the coal face, what makes every member of the team tick, and how they all interact with one another.

So you're a facilitator?

Absolutely. Here to bring out the very best in the talents of my very best resource, the wonderful and highly motivated workforce at the Cull Valley Evening Gazette. At the end of the day, you come back to that key word, empowerment.

What's the biggest problem confronting you at the moment?

As you know, these are difficult times for the regional press, there's even talk that a few evening and daily papers, like the Gazette, could eventually become weeklies. Sadly, we've had to let one or two of our staff go.

How did you go about it? Last in, first out?

No, it's important to hold on to the best people. We opted for a policy of scoring our personnel, via an examination of their skills competencies in a variety of areas. Their ability to communicate effectively, to work well as part of a team, and to adapt to change, that sort of thing.

Any problems with that approach?

There were one or two grumbles, mainly from people who didn't appreciate that this really was a level playing field. It was done in a scrupulously fair manner.

But who did the scoring, and wasn't there a danger of bias or score-settling? Can anyone really be objective?

Look, I realise you've got a job to do but I rather resent that. There was never any danger whatsoever of any score-settling, as you put it. The two people who were tasked and, yes, empowered with this role are individuals of the highest integrity and values, and they were both chosen as absolutely top-class journalists who were disinterested in the best sense, and could have no possible axe to grind.

Can you name them?

If I were to say to you Frances 'Doc' Jekyll and Kenneth 'Chuck' Thrower, I'm sure that would be all the reassurance you need.

Thanks, Mark, that's really clarified a few things for us. Tell us a joke to send us on our way with a smile on our face.

What do you call the deliberate destruction of a 1966 sunburst-red Ford Anglia:

Reggiecide!

A8814, West Yorkshire, 11-27am

That's a cracking gag, Mark, it's the way you tell 'em. You'll be pleased to hear that I've made an inspired choice to replace me as the new editor of the *National Diary*. He's not worked in journalism for a long time but he has got junior editorial experience in the hot seat. Funny how you can fail to see obvious solution when it is staring you in the face.

So – it's over to you, Tom Waterfall…

THE NATIONAL DIARY

Thanks, Teddy. Yes, I'm Tom Waterfall and as the newly appointed man in the hot seat at the *National Diary* I'd like to start with a big thank you to the departing editor. Teddy Beresford has worked tirelessly to bring us two decades of journalistic excellence. During that time *The National Diary* has matured into a much-loved institution. And Teddy certainly left with a bang, a truly superb final edition for September 1.

This isn't my first senior post in newspapers. As some of you might remember, I am a former editor of the *Badger Hill School Telegraph*. That's a while back, of course, since when I've mainly worked in advertising and the film industry, so I really appreciate the faith that Teddy is showing in me.

One new feature of future papers – I hope, by the way, that you like the more modern mast head – will be a greater focus on investigative journalism. We begin today with a hard-hitting piece by me about a recent tragedy in West Yorkshire's Cull Valley....

Love and death in the Pennines
By Tom Waterfall, Editor

No flowers or wreaths have marked the spot where Teddy Beresford and Anthony and Julia Yates died.

This was tragedy handled quietly, and with dignity. No grieving relatives talked at length about the way a wonderful light had gone out of their lives; no heart-broken friends poured out their emotions as they recalled the most special people they had ever known; no one left hand-written messages by the roadside.

Brief statements were issued to the press on behalf of Mr Beresford and Mr and Mrs Yates, Hexroyd coroner Gordon South recorded a verdict of accidental death – it was the third such tragedy in 12 months on a notorious bend of the bleak Pennine road – and the families' wishes to be left to mourn in peace were largely observed.

However, two people understood instinctively that this was unlikely to have been an accident: they were Teddy's parents, Dr Philip and Dr Valerie Beresford. I knew them because I had been a childhood friend of Teddy Beresford. Teddy and I didn't see much of one another after we went to different grammar schools, but I'd retained fond memories of his parents who were very kind to me when my father died. I couldn't get to Teddy's funeral because I was working in New York but my wife Rachel (who had known Teddy as a teenager) and I sent a letter of condolence.

Philip and Valerie wrote back thanking us, and said that they would like to meet me. I visited their large Swiss-chalet style house for the first time in many years and they handed me a disk which contained an extraordinary document called *The National Diary*. It could be described best as a newspaper-style diary kept by their only child.

Teddy had started *The National Diary* when he was 11 and he'd written up his harmless stories (he wins Wimbledon, he plays at Wembley for Hexroyd Park Avenue) until, at the age of 14, adolescence kicks in and he presumably deems it all rather childish. But then, at 17, it all starts again when he writes up the painful account of how he lost to me in a tennis match. *The National Diary* continues in this new, analytical format until Teddy's death.

"This is too painful for us to examine closely, Tom, but the truth about what happened must be in here. Tell us what you make of it, and whether the story can be set straight," Valerie Beresford said when she handed over the disk to me.....

Also inside this special issue:

The write stuff

Two acclaimed authors from the same part of West Yorkshire have published new books this week. *A Fine Line*, by former Hexroyd Grammar School teacher Colin Sangster, looks at single incidents that have changed the course of history, and Henry Hawley's *Voices in the Sky* is being compared to Alain-Fournier's masterpiece *Le Grand Meaulnes* for its evocation of a land of lost content.

Driving into the Valley of Death

The British are coming! Heather Margolis sees Oscar potential in director Tom Waterfall's second theatrical release, *Here in the Cull Valley*, starring John Simm, Claire Foy and Paul Rhys. Read her verdict.

My work on this Earth is done. But before I go, I fancy a trip to the pictures. Let's check *The National Diary* and see if that film's worth watching…

Driving into the Valley of Death

Here in the Cull Valley provides compelling evidence of Cull Valley-born director Tom Waterfall's burgeoning talent, reports arts editor Heather Margolis.
Oscars ahoy?

Tom Waterfall brings a French New Wave sensibility to this powerful drama about love, death and obsession in the north of England.

With its quick scene changes, atmospheric use of location and almost improvised-sounding dialogue, *Here in the Cull Valley* has the verve and style of Truffaut, while recalling Tony Richardson's classic adaptation of *A Taste of Honey*.

But this is no 'kitchen-sink' drama. The original screenplay by Helena Burgess and Waterfall casts an acerbic and witty eye rather higher up the social scale. They show us the devastating fall-out of a bourgeois ménage à trois in a West Yorkshire town which initially looks like a tourist board promotion film, but very quickly becomes darker and more threatening as the inexorable tragedy is set in motion. The colour gradually bleeds out of the picture as we head for a gruesome, sepia, moorland finale. At this point, we have come full circle. However, the film's beginning is not quite its end, because there is a consoling coda.

Here in the Cull Valley begins in the style of a Barbara Vine-Ruth Rendell 'why-dunnit' as Ed (John Simm), Jools (Claire Foy) and her husband Tony (Paul Rhys) plunge to their death in a car. We then learn, in a largely sequential way, what led to this tragedy.

It's a wonderful showcase for British acting talent. John Simm is engaging in the role of Ed, the naïve provincial journalist who gets in way over his head. As Jools, blonde-rinsed Claire Foy is no Little Dorrit. There is something deeply disturbing going on just beneath the expensive make-up. Paul Rhys redefines the term cold fish as repressed architect Tony. Watch out, too, for show-stealing cameos by Russell Dixon and Kathy Burke as Ken and Fran, Ed's weasel-like, backstabbing colleagues.

Funding from the National Lottery and North of Watford Film Finance (NOWFF) made this movie possible. *Here in the Cull Valley* is a low-budget affair although, thanks to Emma Porter's handsome cinematography, you'd never think so. And while I don't want to give too much away, Waterfall has come up with a wonderful subversion of that oldest of movie clichés, the newspaper headline which reveals dramatic plot developments.

Clever enough for the art-house crowd but a gripping piece of entertainment, *Here in the Cull Valley* will surely give the recent dreary and formulaic output from Hollywood a run for its money given a fair crack of the whip.

Distributors please take note.

Here in the Cull Valley, (UK, 97 mins, Cert 15) can be seen at selected cinemas throughout the UK

A8814, West Yorkshire, 11-27am

Look forward to seeing that one, I always thought John Simm was the man for the part. Claire Foy, too. Very interesting. Now, back to The Beatles. How could I possibly have got it so wrong about *Abbey Road*? I've allowed myself to become confused by the *Magical Mystery Tour* which, on reflection, I shouldn't have included. Quick, now, time's running short. What came after *Sgt Pepper*? Christ, how could I have forgotten?

My favourite, the White Album.

Yes, I can see it approaching now. The brilliant White Album.....
So white, white…

CULL VALLEY EVENING GAZETTE

Monday March 1 2010

Baby born in ambulance

By Jeannie Derby

Little Teddy Nolan couldn't wait to meet Mum and Dad.

The seven-pound bundle of joy announced his arrival in the world, one week early, with a few lusty shrieks from the back of an ambulance.

Proud mother Ruth said: "It was all so sudden. I was watching the ten o'clock news with my husband, Rory, when my waters broke, and the contractions became more and more frequent. I'd barely got into the ambulance when it became clear that Teddy was going to be with us before we arrived at the hospital.

"I'm just glad we'd cancelled our plans for a night-out at the theatre, Teddy was due in seven days' time and we thought we might be pushing our luck."

By a further stroke of good fortune, off-duty midwife Sally Merrens, a recent arrival in the Cull Valley, is a near-neighbour of the Nolans. She joined the ambulance crew just in case things started to happen quickly. That's exactly how it worked out but Sally said: "To be honest, there's no real drama to report, it must have been one of the easiest deliveries I've ever been involved with. Rory was in a bit of a panic but Ruth took it all in her stride."

Ruth and Rory have already decided on the baby's name, in memory of their friend Teddy Beresford, the former *Gazette* journalist who died tragically last summer in a car accident on the A8814 Ainsley-Hexroyd road.

There has been no shortage of visitors wanting to meet the new arrival, at the Nolans' delightful eighteenth century converted barn outside Hexroyd, overlooking the moors.

Among them, of course, has been Sally who is looking forward to being an honorary auntie. She says: "Teddy is absolutely gorgeous. You can already tell that he's going to be a real lady killer."

Other novels, novellas and short story collections available from Stairwell Books

Carol's Christmas	N.E. David
Feria	N.E. David
A Day at the Races	N.E. David
Running With Butterflies	John Walford
Foul Play	P J Quinn
Poison Pen	P J Quinn
Rosie and John's Magical Adventure	The Children of Ryedale District Primary Schools
Wine Dark, Sea Blue	A.L. Michael
Skydive	Andrew Brown
Close Disharmony	P J Quinn
When the Crow Cries	Maxine Ridge
The Geology of Desire	Clint Wastling
Homelands	Shaunna Harper
Border 7	Pauline Kirk
Tales from a Prairie Journal	Rita Jerram
How to be a Man	Alan Smith

For further information please contact rose@stairwellbooks.com

www.stairwellbooks.co.uk
@stairwellbooks